Table of Contents

Copyright 1987, Instructional Fair, Inc.

Why did Yankee Doodle call a feather "Macaroni"?

In the early 1700's, some wealthy and lazy young Englishmen started the Macaroni Club. Members of the club copied French customs and ate French foods. Soon the English started to use the word "macaroni" to make fun of anything that was copied from the French. At the same time, the American colonists were buying more French products and less English products. The angry English traders made fun of the Americans by calling them Yankee Doodle Dandies. The song "Yankee Doodle" was originally an English song. The line, "stuck a feather in his cap and called it macaroni," meant that a Yankee Doodle was foolish enough to think that just sticking a feather in his cap would make him look like a well-dressed Frenchman. The British troops sang "Yankee Doodle" to mock the Americans as they attacked Lexington and Concord in April, 1755. The colonists quickly forced the British to retreat. As the colonial troops forced the British back toward Boston, they began to mock the English by singing "Yankee Doodle." From that time, Americans have taken pride in being Yankees.

Why did Yankee Doodle call a feather "Macaroni"?

Underline another good title for this story.

"Macaroni"

English Traders

Customs of the French People

Underline the main idea of the story.

The English used the term "macaroni" to make fun of anything copied from the French.

"Yankee Doodle" was a popular song during the American Revolution.

English traders used the term "Yankee Doodle Dandies" to make fun of the Americans.

Match.

copy	inhabitants of a colony
colonists	to imitate
mock	to withdraw
retreat	to laugh at; ridicule

Circle.

T   F   Today, most Americans are proud to be called Yankees.

T   F   The Macaroni Club tried to copy French customs.

T   F   The English wanted the Americans to buy French products.

Check the three that apply.

Macaroni . . .

____ was the name of an English club.

____ meant that something was copied from the French.

____ was used as a compliment by most Englishmen.

____ was used as an insult by most Englishmen.

____ was a kind of feather.

What is the Purple Heart?

The Purple Heart is awarded to American soldiers for bravery. It was originated in 1782 by George Washington. The first Purple Heart was called the "Badge of Military Merit." It was made of purple fabric trimmed with white lace and sewn permanently onto the soldier's jacket. It was awarded to only three soldiers of the American Revolution. The men who were awarded the Purple Heart were granted certain tokens of military respect usually reserved for high ranking officers. The Badge of Military Merit was discontinued after the American Revolution. In fact, military badges of any kind were rarely given by the United States government until the time of the Civil War, when the Medal of Honor was established by an act of Congress.

The Purple Heart was revived in 1932 and awarded to honor World War I veterans who had been extremely brave soldiers. Since 1942, the Purple Heart has been awarded to all soldiers severely wounded in the line of duty. The Purple Heart that is now awarded is a gold-colored heart with purple enamel and has a profile of George Washington. It hangs on a purple ribbon edged in white.

What is the Purple Heart?

Underline another good title for this story.

The Story of the Purple Heart

The Medal of Honor

The Story of the Purple Heart's Design

Underline the main idea of the story.

The Purple Heart hangs on a purple ribbon edged in white.

The Purple Heart is awarded to American soldiers for bravery.

The Badge of Military Merit was discontinued after the American Revolution.

Match.

profile	lasting forever
originated	side view of a person's face
permanent	sign; mark; symbol
token	where or when something began; started

Circle.

T   F   Only two soldiers received the Badge of Military Merit.

T   F   George Washington received the first Purple Heart.

T   F   The Purple Heart has been given since the time of the American Revolution.

Check the two that apply.

The Purple Heart . . .

_____ was originally called the Badge of Military Merit.

_____ was first awarded during the Civil War.

_____ is now given to soldiers who are severely wounded.

_____ is made of solid gold.

5

Who said, "Go West, young man"?

Horace Greeley (1811–1872) was a newspaperman of the middle 1800's. Some people thought his articles were too opinionated. But Greeley believed that the news should always tell the whole truth. He wrote and printed articles about things that he believed would help people make the world better. In the middle 1850's, it was especially hard for young people to find jobs. Greeley believed that young people could build a good life for themselves if they moved to the West. He wrote an article that told poor but hardworking young people to "turn your face to the Great West, and there build up a home and fortune." In later articles, he often suggested to young people to "Go West, young man, and grow up with the country." People were impressed by these articles. But Greeley knew he could not take all the credit for the idea. He wrote an article explaining that he had gotten the phrase from an 1851 newspaper article by John Babsone Lane Soule. Soule was really the first person who printed the expression, "Go West, young man."

Who said, "Go West, young man"?

Underline another good title for this story.

Who Was Horace Greeley?

Job Opportunities in the 1850's

Newspaper Reporters

Underline the main idea of the story.

Horace Greeley was a newspaperman of the middle 1800's who wrote many articles telling young people to move west.

John Babsone Lane Soule was really the first man to use the expression, "Go West, young man."

Many people thought Greeley's articles were too opinionated.

Match.

fortune	stubbornly holding to personal opinion
opinionated	wealth; riches
credit	a piece or section in a newspaper, dealing with a single subject
article	acknowledgement of work done or help given

Circle.

T   F   Horace Greeley was the first to say, "Go West, young man."

T   F   Horace Greeley believed that there was opportunity in the West.

Check the three that apply.

Horace Greeley . . .

____ felt a newspaper could be used to help people.

____ moved west when he was young.

____ wrote articles encouraging young people to move west.

____ wanted people he didn't like to move west.

____ was a newspaperman.

What do "SOS" and "Mayday" really mean?

    SOS and Mayday are both international signals of distress. SOS is the international radio signal of distress. It does not stand for "save our ship," nor was it originally a Morse code signal. The distress signal of three dots, three dashes, and three dots was first recommended at a radio telegraph conference in 1906 because it was an easy telegraph signal to remember, easy to send, and easy to recognize. It was adopted in 1908. The signal is not sent as a series of SOS's, but continually as three dots, three dashes, three dots, three dashes, three dots, and so on.

    Mayday is the international distress signal used in voice transmission. It was based on the French expression, "m'aidez" (pronounced mā' dā'), which means "help me." At the time Mayday came into use as a distress signal, French was a language that educated people all over the world were likely to understand. And m'aidez, or Mayday, is easy to say even when someone is in great trouble. It also travels easily over the air waves and is easily recognized.

What do "SOS" and "Mayday" really mean?

Underline another good title for this story.

International Distress Signals

Dashes and Dots

How to Get Help

Underline the main idea of the story.

Mayday is the international distress signal used in voice transmission.

The SOS distress signal was first recommended at a radio telegraph conference.

SOS and Mayday are both international signals of distress.

Match.

recommend	between two or more nations
international	passing from one person or place to another
distress	danger; difficulty
transmission	to favorably suggest

Circle.

T   F   The SOS distress signal was adopted in 1806.

T   F   SOS is the abbreviation for "save our ship."

T   F   Mayday is based on the French expression meaning "help me."

Check the two that apply.

SOS . . .

____ is a convenient name for . . . ‒‒‒ . . . ‒‒‒ .

____ was originally based on Morse code.

____ and Mayday are both international signals of distress.

Why is the bald eagle our national symbol?

When the United States became independent of Great Britain, the Congress had to do many things to show that the United States was finally and truly a separate country. One thing they had to do was to design a national emblem. Because other national emblems included an animal, the Congress of 1782 felt our emblem should include an animal. Many animals unique to the United States were considered. Benjamin Franklin, for one, felt that the turkey should be on the national emblem because of its importance as a food source for the early colonists, because it was so plentiful, and because it was unique to the United States. However, the eagle was finally chosen because it had always been considered a symbol of power. The bald, or white headed eagle, was chosen because it was native only to North America.

On the emblem, the eagle is clutching several spears in its feet, ready for defense. An olive branch, a symbol of peace, is also carried in the eagle's feet. Another olive branch frames the eagle. The emblem stands for peace and strength for defense if necessary.

Why is the bald eagle our national symbol?

Underline another good title for this story.

The National Emblem of the U.S.

The Congress of 1782

The Contributions of Benjamin Franklin

Underline the main idea of the story.

The Congress of 1782 designed a national emblem to show that the U.S. was truly a separate country.

An olive branch, symbol of peace, is carried in the eagle's feet on our national emblem.

The bald eagle was chosen as our national symbol because it has always been considered a symbol of power and because it is native only to North America.

Match.

independent	existing or growing naturally in a particular region or country
native	to grip with hands or claws
plentiful	not under another's control or rule
clutch	abundant; ample

Circle.

T   F   The olive branch is a symbol of strength.

T   F   The bald eagle is really bald.

T   F   The eagle has always been considered a symbol of power.

Check the two that apply.

The bald eagle . . .

____ is a symbol of war.

____ is a symbol of strength.

____ is a symbol of peace.

____ is the largest bird in the U.S.

____ is native only to North America.

11

Who are the gypsies?

Gypsies are a group of people who live as nomads, traveling from place to place. They travel in groups of several related families and usually wear brightly colored clothing and a lot of jewelry. They are craftsmen, traders, musicians, dancers, circus performers, and fortune tellers. Gypsies have been living in various European countries since the 1500's. Gypsies have lived in the United States since 1715. Because similar groups lived in Egypt, and because the nomadic people arriving in Europe resembled Egyptians in general, Europeans thought that they had come originally from Egypt. Europeans called these dark-haired, dark-eyed wanderers, ``gypsies''– short for Egyptians.

Gypsies have adopted customs and some language from places where they travel. But many gypsies also speak a language called Romany which is similar to the Indian language called Sanskrit. It is now believed that gypsies originally came from India and wandered away from there around 1300 A.D. Very few true gypsies remain because laws forbid them from traveling through certain areas. Gypsies are being forced to change their way of life.

Who are the gypsies?

Underline another good title for this story.

Gypsies – A Wandering People

Why Gypsies Travel

The Native Gypsy Homeland

Underline the main idea of the story.

Gypsies have been living in various European countries since the 1500's.

Many gypsies speak a language called Romany, which is similar to the Indian language called Sanskrit.

Gypsies are a group of people who move from place to place.

Match.

adopt	someone who wanders from place to place
resemble	to command someone not to do something
nomad	to take as one's own
forbid	to look like

Circle.

T F Gypsies have lived in the United States since 1715.

T F Gypsies are wandering Egyptians.

T F Gypsies probably originally came from India.

Check the two that apply.

Gypsies . . .

_____ are nomads.

_____ are mainly farmers.

_____ look similar to Egyptians.

_____ do not live in the United States.

Where did tulips originate?

Tulips are native to central Asia. Well over 100 kinds are known to grow wild in the countries of Nepal, Iran, Afghanistan, and Turkey. European explorers and traders brought tulips from Turkey in the 1500's. Tulips require the type of cold winters typical in Europe in order to grow and bloom in spring. The climate of the Netherlands is especially well suited for growing tulips. By the 1600's, the tulip was becoming a national hobby in the Netherlands.

People collected many different varieties of tulips in their gardens. People invested in rare and beautiful tulips hoping to make a profit from other collectors. Some people in the Netherlands were actually investing their life savings in rare tulips. For a while in the 1600's, so many people in the Netherlands spent so much of their time and money on tulips that other work and industry suffered. The country might have gone bankrupt if the government had not regulated investments in tulips. Once the government stepped in, tulip production quickly became a profitable source of world trade for the Netherlands.

Underline another good title for this story.

Different Varieties of Flowers

Home of the Tulips

Climate of the Netherlands

Underline the main idea of the story.

The climate of the Netherlands is especially good for tulips.

Tulips are native to central Asia, but they quickly became popular in the Netherlands.

The Netherlands might have gone bankrupt had the government not regulated investments in tulips.

Match.

nativo   a varied assortment

hobby   existing or growing naturally in a
                                particular region

variety   a favorite pastime

Circle.

T   F   Tulips require a cold winter in order to grow in the spring.

T   F   Tulips are native to Holland.

T   F   Tulips are native to several central Asian countries.

Check the three that apply.

The Netherlands . . .

____ began growing tulips in the 1500's.

____ was nearly financially ruined because of tulips.

____ actually grows very few tulips.

____ grows many kinds of tulips.

What was the Santa Fe Trail?

SANTA FE TRAIL

FRANKLIN

SANTA FE

    The Santa Fe Trail was the route traveled by traders from Franklin, Missouri to Santa Fe, New Mexico. It was never an actual road. Instead, it was a general route that led from one water source to another across Nebraska, Wyoming, the panhandles of Oklahoma and Texas, and into what is now New Mexico. Between southwestern Nebraska and Santa Fe, there were actually two main routes. The spring route led through the steep foothills of the Rockies. The fall route led across fifty miles of the Cimmeron Desert.

    Sante Fe was originally a Mexican mission town. Once Mexico was freed from Spain in 1820, people of Santa Fe were anxious to trade their Mexican silver for American goods. William Becknell of Franklin, Missouri was one of the the first to trade with the mission. His first trading venture was such a success that each year from 1822 to 1843, trading parties set out from Franklin bound for Santa Fe. Trade stopped during the Mexican War. But after the war, Santa Fe was in American territory and trade was resumed. The Santa Fe Trail was one of the main western routes used during the Gold Rush.

Underline another good title for this story.

Trading in Santa Fe

The Santa Fe Trail—Route of Trade and Travel

A Mexican Trade Route

Underline the main idea of the story.

William Becknell was one of the first people to trade with the Mexican people.

The Santa Fe Trail was the route traveled by traders from Franklin, Missouri to Santa Fe, New Mexico.

The spring route of the Santa Fe Trail led through the steep foothills of the Rockies.

Match.

source   excited or eager

steep   place where something is obtained

anxious   to continue after an interruption

resume   having a sharp slope

Circle.

T   F   There was only one main route for the Santa Fe Trail.

T   F   The Santa Fe Trail was first traveled in 1849.

T   F   The Santa Fe Trail was a trade route.

Check the two that apply.

The Santa Fe Trail . . .

_____ was only a gravel road.

_____ was used mainly by traders.

_____ was first traveled by the Mexicans.

_____ led from Franklin, Missouri to Santa Fe.

What is a patent?

Whenever people invent items that they would like to manufacture and sell, they must apply for a "patent." A patent is an official government document which grants the holder the sole right to manufacture the item that he has invented. Our patent laws state that the government will prosecute anyone who copies an item that has been patented.

Governments of each country grant patents. Each country has its own patent laws. Most governments require that detailed plans and drawings of an invention be registered with the government patent office. The government can then make a study to verify that no one else already has a patent for the same invention. If two people submit very similar plans at about the same time, the person who submitted his plan first will be granted a patent. The other inventor must make considerable changes in order to be granted a patent.

When the United States grants a patent, the inventor is protected by law against competition for seventeen years. Some patents can be extended for longer periods of time. Each patent is given a number. The patent number must appear on each patented item that is sold. Patent protection laws indirectly encourage people to invent new and better products.

What is a patent?

Underline another good title for this story.

The Importance of a Patent

Government Regulations

Patent Numbers

Underline the main idea of the story.

A patent protects an inventor against competition for seventeen years.

Patent protection laws indirectly encourage people to invent new and better products.

A patent is an official government document that grants the holder the sole right to manufacture an item which he has invented.

Match.

document	carry on a legal action against an accused person to prove his guilt
sole	single; only
prosecute	rivalry
competition	anything written or printed that is used to record information or to prove something

Circle.

T   F   A patent number must appear on each patented item that is sold.

T   F   A patent protects inventors from competition forever.

Check the three that apply.

Patents . . .

____ are issued by governments of each country.

____ can be granted by a state.

____ protect an invention from competition for seventeen years.

____ are never extended for more than seventeen years.

____ are regulated by laws.

How did the guillotine get its name?

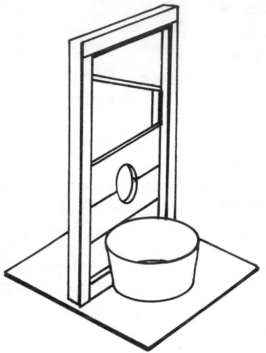

A lot of people believe that the guillotine was invented by a Frenchman named Guillotin and that the guillotine was named for its inventor. Actually, there is no record of who invented the original beheading device. But a simple beheading device was in use in Italy in the 1400's. In the 1700's, a French doctor named Louis improved it. For many years, the beheading device was known as the Louison. But the Louison was seldom used because it was customary to use various means of torture to execute criminals. Late in the 1700's, a French doctor named Joseph Ignace Guillotin began to campaign for more humane executions. He believed that the Louison was the least painful way to execute criminals. It took a long time to convince the government to abandon tortuous executions. By the time the beheading device became the official means of execution, the Louison had become known as the guillotine. The guillotine was used to kill thousands of people during the French Revolution. The Guillotin family was so shamed and saddened by this that they changed their name.

How did the guillotine get its name?

Underline another good title for this story.

The Development of the Guillotine

The French Revolution

The Inventor of the Guillotine

Underline the main idea of the story.

Dr. Guillotin campaigned for more humane methods of executions.

There is no record of the inventor of the guillotine, but, it received its name from the French doctor who campaigned for its use.

The guillotine was used to kill thousands of people during the French Revolution.

Match.

abandon	to inflict severe pain
torture	to put to death
execute	showing mercy
humane	to give up completely

Check the two that apply.

The guillotine . . .

____ was the first beheading device.

____ was used in France in the 1300's.

____ is a relatively painless means of execution.

____ became the official means of execution in France.

____ was a source of pride to the Guillotin family.

What is the origin of the word "curfew"?

The English word "curfew" is based on an old French term "cuevre-feu" which means "cover the fire." The expression started more than 1,000 years ago. At that time, each house had a big, open fireplace to provide both heat to warm the house and heat for cooking. Many of the houses were built of wood and had straw roofs. Such houses would burn easily. The houses in a village were close together. If one house caught on fire at night, a whole village might be burned. Town leaders passed laws that made people put out their fires and cover them with cooled ashes before they went to bed. Each evening, a bell was rung as warning that it was time to "cover the fire." If someone was working outside or visiting with a neighbor, he had to hurry home to cover his fire.

The bell meant "cover the fire," but it also caused everyone to go home. People seldom went out again after the "cuevre-feu" bell rang. Eventually, the word "curfew" was used to mean a time when people must get off the streets.

What is the origin of the word "curfew"?

Underline another good title for this story.

Curfews as a Safety Device

Village Fires

The Evening Bell

Underline the main idea of the story.

The English word "curfew" is based on an old French term meaning "cover the fire."

A thousand years ago, most homes were built of wood and had straw roofs.

Today, curfew is a time when people must get off the streets.

Match.

expression	not very often; rarely
provide	advance notice; a word of caution
seldom	a saying
warning	to furnish; equip

Circle.

T　F　A thousand years ago, people had very small fireplaces.

T　F　"Cuevre-feu" used to mean "time to go home for dinner."

T　F　The word "curfew" is based on an old French expression.

Check the two that apply.

Long ago, cuevre-feu (curfew) . . .

_____ was the time to cover the fire.

_____ was signaled by a bell.

_____ was a good time to cook dinner.

_____ told people they must go to bed.

23 Copyright 1987, Instructional Fair, Inc.

Were oranges named for their color?

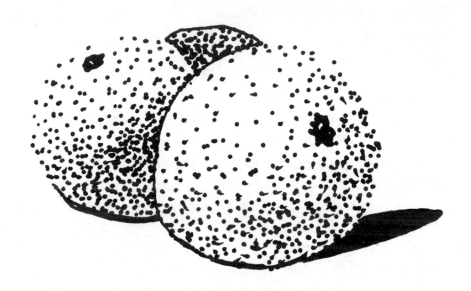

The orange was not named for its color. Actually, the color orange gets its name from the reddish-yellow fruit known to us as the orange. The Persians (Iranians) were the first to cultivate oranges. The ancient Persian word for the orange fruit was pronounced "narange." Spanish explorers and traders brought oranges to Europe and pronounced its name "naranja." The French dropped the initial "n" from naranja because of a misunderstanding. They thought the Spanish were saying "un oranja" (an orange). The end of "naranja" was too harsh for the French. They called the reddish-yellow fruit, "un orange."

The French introduced oranges to the English. At that time, the English had no word for the color orange. Very few things are naturally orange in color and orange dyes had not been invented. Red, yellow, and reddish-yellow were sufficient to describe the color of such things as the sun, flowers, and red hair. The color of the orange was so striking that people started comparing the color of other reddish-yellow things to the orange.

Were oranges named for their color?

Underline another good title for this story.

Orange—Color or Fruit?

How to Cultivate Oranges

Orange Dyes

Underline the main idea of the story.

Oranges were first cultivated by the Persians.

The color orange got its name from the fruit known to us as the orange.

Very few things are naturally orange in color, so orange dyes had to be invented.

Match.

cultivate	a failure to understand correctly
misunderstanding	raise crops by tilling, by labor, or care
dye	very noticeable
striking	material used for coloring

Circle.

T   F   The French introduced oranges to the Persians.

T   F   Oranges are called oranges because they are orange.

T   F   The color name orange comes from the name of the orange fruit.

Check the two that apply.

Oranges . . .

_____ were cultivated first in France.

_____ were cultivated first in Persia.

_____ are called oranges in every language.

_____ gave the color orange its name.

_____ are named after the color orange.

What does "O.K." stand for?

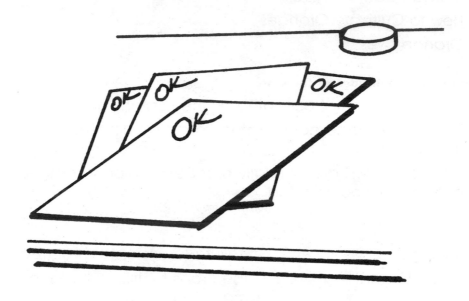

In the early 1800's, many students and writers misspelled words just for the fun of it. It was also custom to use only initial letters of common expressions. "O.K." may have started as the initials for "oll korrect." "Oll korrect" was the silly way to spell "all correct." Andrew Jackson (1767–1845) used "O.K." on many of his papers. But he did not spell well, and many of his political opponents did not think he was well-educated enough to be president. They said he simply did not even know how to spell "all correct."

"O.K." may have come from another language. English-speaking Americans use many Indian words. The Choctaw used the word "okee" to mean "it is settled." The one word stands for a whole idea. There is no English word that means exactly the same thing. Perhaps English-speaking Americans repeated the Indian word to show that they agreed about something. There is also a Jamaican expression, "oh ki," which means about the same things as "O.K." Perhaps English-speaking Americans learned the word from Jamaican slaves.

Underline another good title for this story.

"O.K."—an Indian Expression

"O.K."—a Worldwide Expression

Jamaican Slaves

Underline the main idea of the story.

There are many theories about the origin and meaning of "O.K."

"Oll korrect" was the silly way to spell "all correct."

Some people did not think Andrew Jackson was well-educated enough to be president.

Match.

custom	one who opposes; adversary
political	a saying
expression	of or having to do with government or politics
opponent	habit or accepted way of doing things

Circle.

T   F   "Okee" means "it is settled."

T   F   The initials for "oll korrect" are definitely "O.K."

T   F   "O.K." might be the initials of "oll korrect."

Check the two that apply.

"O.K." might have . . .

____ come from a Choctaw word.

____ come from a Jamaican word.

____ started in 1950.

What is Welsh rabbit?

Welsh rabbit is a seasoned cheese sauce served over toast. In feudal times, there was a law in Wales that forbade Welsh peasants from hunting the game on the estates where they lived and worked. Hunting rabbits and other game was a privilege reserved for noblemen. Ingenious Welsh peasants concocted a tasty cheese sauce and served it on toast. They jokingly called the dish Welsh rabbit because they were sure it was better than the rabbit they were not allowed to hunt and eat. And its appearance resembled the sauces sometimes made from real rabbits. In addition to sharp cheese, Welsh rabbit had cream or ale, salt, pepper, mustard, and other seasonings.

The sauce was so good that it became a popular dish at some of the English inns and pubs. Many English authors, including Charles Dickens, have mentioned Welsh rabbit in their writings. People all over the world still serve versions of Welsh rabbit. Americans usually refer to Welsh rabbit as "Welsh rarebit."

What is Welsh rabbit?

Underline another good title for this story.

Famous English Authors

The Peasants' Answer to Real Rabbit

Hunting Laws in Wales

Underline the main idea of the story.

Welsh rabbit is a seasoned cheese sauce served over toast that was used as a substitute by the peasants in feudal times for sauces made from real rabbits.

In feudal times, hunting rabbit and other game was a privilege reserved for noblemen.

Many English writers have mentioned Welsh rabbit in their writings.

Match.

feudal	made more pleasant to the taste by use of spices or flavorings
seasoned	prepare by combining ingredients
ingenious	having to do with medieval times in Europe
concoct	skillful; inventive

Circle.

T   F   Hunting rabbits and other game was a privilege reserved for noblemen.

T   F   Welsh rabbit is a cheese sauce served over toast.

T   F   Welsh rabbit was very rare and hard to find.

Check the three that apply.

Welsh rabbit . . .

_____ was invented by American chefs.

_____ has been eaten in England for a long time.

_____ was named as a joke.

_____ contains cream or ale.

_____ was invented for noblemen.

Was there really a Lady Godiva?

There really was a woman named Lady Godiva. Actually, her name was Godgifu which means "God's gift." She lived in England during the eleventh century. Lady Godiva was the wife of Earl Leofric, who was also Lord of Coventry. (Coventry is a city in England.) According to legend, Lady Godiva believed that the taxes imposed by her husband, the Earl, were too high. The Earl teased Lady Godiva by saying he would lower taxes when she rode through town naked. Lady Godiva took him seriously. She asked the townspeople to stay inside on the day of her ride. Then, covered only by her long blond hair, Lady Godiva rode through town on a white horse. Taxes were lowered. According to the legend, only one man, Tom, peeked. This is where we get the expression, "peeping Tom."

The ride may have happened, or it may be only a colorful legend. No known written record was made at the time. The earliest known written record of Lady Godiva's ride was made in the thirteenth century by a Benedictine monk at St. Albans.

Was there really a Lady Godiva?

Underline another good title for this story.

The Story of Lady Godiva's Ride

Riding to Raise Taxes

A Colorful Legend

Underline the main idea of the story.

Godgifu means "God's gift."

A Benedictine monk wrote the story of Lady Godiva in the thirteenth century.

According to legend, Lady Godiva rode through the town naked in order to lower taxes.

Match.

century   a saying

legend   charged or taxed

imposed   a story handed down for centuries and
                   believed to have a historical basis

expression   period of 100 years

Circle.

T   F   Lady Godiva lived in England during the eleventh century.

T   F   The story of Lady Godiva is definitely a legend.

T   F   The story of Lady Godiva is definitely true.

Check the three that apply.

Lady Godgifu . . .

____ was the real name of Lady Godiva.

____ was married to Earl Leofric, Lord of Coventry.

____ was made up by a Benedictine monk.

____ lived during the eleventh century.

What is a scarab?

A scarab is a type of beetle which was sacred to the ancient Egyptians. The scarab beetle has some unusual habits that caused the ancient Egyptians to consider them symbols of life after death. Scarab beetles breed in dung. They form cow dung into round pellets and roll the pellets into their underground burrows. Scarab beetles lay their eggs in these dung pellets. When the scarab larvae hatch, they live on the nutrients in the dung pellets.

The Egyptians thought the pellets were symbols of the world. Just as the world appears to die each winter and experience rebirth each spring, the dung comes to life again when the scarab larvae hatch and grow. The Egyptians also believed that the sun was the source of all life. They believed that the scarab represented the sun because the scarab's head resembled the sun and its rays of light.

The Egyptians carved symbolic scarabs from stone and cast symbolic scarabs in gold and other precious metals. The scarabs were worn as sacred charms. Beautiful, jeweled scarab charms were buried with the dead.

What is a scarab?

Underline another good title for this story.

A Symbol of Life After Death

Nutrients in Cow Dung

Egyptian Jewels

Underline the main idea of the story.

A scarab is a type of beetle which was sacred to the ancient Egyptians because it was considered a symbol of life after death.

Symbolic scarabs made of stone or precious metals were worn as sacred charms.

The Egyptians believed the sun to be the source of all life.

Match.

sacred	manure
symbol	holy; entitled to respect and reverence
dung	anything nutritious or having food value
nutrient	that which stands for or suggests something else

Circle.

T   F   The Egyptians thought the pellets were symbols of the world.

T   F   A scarab is a type of cow.

T   F   Egyptians used scarabs as symbols of life after death.

Check the three that apply.

Scarabs . . .

____ are beetles that lay their eggs in cow dung pellets.

____ were believed to represent the sun.

____ were believed to represent the world.

____ were believed to represent life after death.

____ die and are reborn.

What is the "pigeon drop"?

The "pigeon drop" is a very old type of "confidence game." A confidence game is a trick a criminal uses to swindle someone. The person who is swindled is the "pigeon." The confidence criminal is a "bunko artist." The bunko artist looks for a lonely pigeon who can be tempted to do something dishonest in order to get money. One version of a pigeon drop works something like this. The friendly bunko artist gains the pigeon's confidence and friendship. Then he tells the pigeon that he has found a lot of money but cannot spend it because the owner may have given a list of serial numbers to the police. The bunko artist asks the pigeon to loan him money to live on until the police might forget about the money. He promises to exchange two dollars for every dollar the pigeon will loan him. They agree on an amount and plan to exchange bags of money in a public place. The pigeon trades real money for fake money. The pigeon must wait until he is alone to count his money. Then it is too late. Different criminals use different versions of this swindle.

What is the "pigeon drop"?

Underline another good title for this story.

How to Swindle a Bunko Artist

Feeding Pigeons

A Confidence Swindle

Underline the main idea of the story.

The criminal must gain the confidence of the pigeon.

The "pigeon drop" is a trick criminals use to swindle people.

The bunko artist asks a pigeon to loan him money to live on.

Match.

confidence game   one guilty of a crime

swindle   to give or take one thing in return
for another

exchange   to cheat out of

criminal   a swindle that takes place by
gaining the trust or confidence of
someone

Circle.

T   F   A victim is called a dove.

T   F   The pigeon drop is a swindle.

T   F   The pigeon drop is a way to steal money.

Check the two that apply.

A bunko artist . . .

_____ is a confidence criminal.

_____ would make a fine neighbor.

_____ robs people by tricking them.

35

Who invented breakfast cereals?

Dr. John Harvey Kellogg and William Keith Kellogg invented several grain products which are now used as breakfast cereals. Dr. John Harvey Kellogg directed the Battle Creek (Michigan) Sanitarium which was also known as the Health Reform Institute. Kellogg believed that many illnesses could be cured by a proper diet. He believed that a simple diet without liquor, coffee, tea, spices, or meat was good for people's health.

Dr. John tried to find tasty ways to serve vegetables and cereals. He invented granola. After many experiments, he and William Keith Kellogg made tasty flakes from wheat by boiling wheat, then flattening it through a roller, and finally toasting it. Soon C. W. Post started the first breakfast cereal company and marketed the wheat flakes as Post Toasties.

In 1898, after many arguments with his brother, William decided to leave the Sanitarium and start another cereal company. He set up the Toasted Corn Flake Company. Cornflakes, All Bran, and Rice Krispies were some of his breakfast cereals.

Who invented breakfast cereals?

Underline another good title for this story.

Health Clinics

The History of Breakfast Cereals

Granola and Other Grain Products

Underline the main idea of the story.

C. W. Post started the first breakfast cereal company.

Cornflakes, All Bran, and Rice Krispies were some of William Kellogg's first breakfast cereals.

Besides other accomplishments, Dr. John Kellogg and William Kellogg invented several grain products that are now used as breakfast cereals.

Match.

toast	make available for selling
flatten	what someone usually eats or drinks
diet	to make or become flat
market	to brown the surface of something

Circle.

T   F   Dr. John Harvey Kellogg invented granola.

T   F   The first cereal company was started by John Kellogg.

Check the two that apply.

John H. Kellogg . . .

____ directed a health institute.

____ believed that people should eat more meat.

____ lived and worked in Battle Creek, Michigan.

____ founded the Toasted Corn Flake Company.

Who invented the zipper?

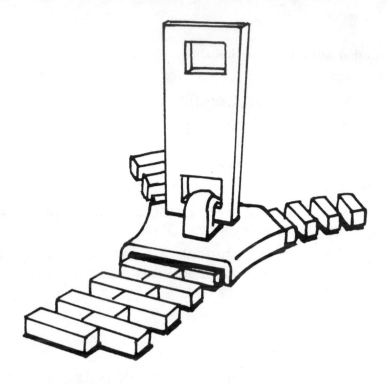

   Whitcomb L. Judson invented the first zipper. He called his invention the "Clasp Locker and Unlocker for Shoes." The original Clasp Locker and Unlocker for Shoes was rather bulky compared to the zippers we now use. It was hard to manufacture and clumsy to use. In 1905, Judson patented an improved fastener and called it the "C-curity." The C-curity was also clumsy and had a tendency to open at the middle. In 1913, a Swedish engineer named Gideon Sunback working for Judson, made several improvements on the C-curity. The fastener made by Sunback looked and worked very much like the metal zippers we now use.

   Clothing companies did not use the metal fasteners. But in the early 1920's, the B.F. Goodrich company started using the slide fastener in their galoshes. Their galoshes were called "Zippers." And that is how the C-curity Slide Fastener become known as the zipper. Whitcomb L. Judson patented many inventions for the first cars and railroads. He might be surprised that the zipper is his most useful invention.

The Homework Booklet IFO165 — 38 —

Who invented the zipper?

Underline another good title for this story.

The Development of the Zipper

The Clasp Locker and Unlocker for Shoes

The B.F. Goodrich Galoshes

Underline the main idea of the story.

Whitcomb L. Judson invented the first zipper and also patented many inventions for the first cars and railroads.

The B.F. Goodrich Company called galoshes "zippers."

The original zipper was called a clasp locker and was rather clumsy and hard to manufacture.

Match.

clumsy	overshoes; boots
tendency	protected by an official document
galoshes	an inclination to act in a certain way
patented	awkward; not handy

Circle.

T   F   The first zipper was very bulky compared to the zipper we now use.

T   F   B.F. Goodrich invented the zipper.

T   F   Zippers got their name from Whitcomb L. Judson.

Check the two that apply.

Whitcomb L. Judson . . .

_____ worked for B.F. Goodrich.

_____ worked for Gideon Sunback.

_____ invented the C-curity Slide Fastener.

_____ patented inventions for cars and railroads.

_____ was a clothing manufacturer.

Who invented the elevator?

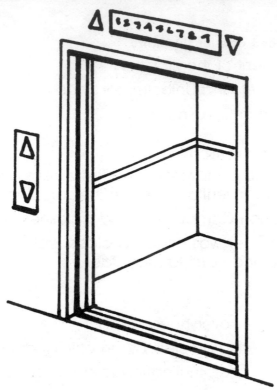

Elisha Graves Otis (1811–1861) invented the first safe elevator. Even in Biblical times, people knew how to use pulleys to raise heavy weights. And in the nineteeth century, factories in Europe and the United States raised freight on platforms. These were not safe for people because the pulley ropes and chains sometimes broke. But in 1852, Otis invented an elevator safety device. Otis' elevator was designed to stop automatically in case the lifting rope or chain broke. In 1854, he demonstrated the safety elevator at a New York exhibition. The demonstration was dramatic. Otis stood alone on the platform as it was hoisted to its highest point. Then the hoisting rope was cut. Everyone expected the platform to crash. But, instead, the platform was stopped by Otis' safety device.

After that, hotel owners were anxious to install safety elevators. They used to have to charge less for rooms on upper floors because of the long walk up the stairs. Now, they could charge extra because the view was better up high and there was less noise at the higher levels.

Underline another good title for this story.

A Dramatic Exhibition

Charging More for Hotel Rooms

The First Safe Elevator

Underline the main idea of the story.

Hotel owners could charge more for rooms on upper floors after the invention of the safety elevator.

Elisha Graves Otis designed an elevator that would stop automatically in case the lifting rope or chain broke.

In 1854, Otis demonstrated the safety elevator at a New York exhibition.

Match.

device	to lift into the air
demonstrate	to show how something works
hoist	eager
anxious	a tool or machine that has a special purpose

Circle.

T   F   Some elevators are raised by ropes or chains.

T   F   Hoisting devices have been used for thousands of years.

T   F   Elisha Graves Otis invented the elevator in 1811.

Check the two that apply.

Elevators . . .

____ were invented in 1854.

____ were improved greatly by Benjamin Franklin.

____ were made safe by Otis.

____ were raised by pulleys.

Crossword Comprehension Review

Across

1. International signal of distress.

4. A type of beetle that was sacred to the ancient Egyptians.

5. Another name for the Louison, a beheading device.

7. All the processes by which the body breaks down the food we eat into nutrients needed by the cells.

9. The result of the body's failure to circulate blood properly.

12. Who suggested to young people "Go West, young man, and grow with the country"?

16. He started the first breakfast cereal company.

17. A group of people who live as nomads, traveling from place to place.

18. Who invented the first safe elevator?

19. All the processes by which the body takes in and uses oxygen and rids itself of carbon dioxide wastes.

20. A badly enlarged thyroid gland.

Down

2. _____ acids make up proteins.

3. An official government document which grants the holder the sole right to manufacture the invented item.

6. Elements which cannot be produced by living things.

8. _____ speed up certain chemical changes in living things.

10. The Purple _____ is awarded to American soldiers for bravery.

11. William _____ left the Battle Creek Sanitarium and started a cereal company.

13. The B.F. Goodrich company called the galoshes it made _____.

14. He invented the first zipper.

15. Protein, a very important kind of _____, helps our bodies grow.

TUTOR'S GUIDE

I Love Reading — Level 6 Book 2

The answer section has been placed in the center of this Homework Booklet so that it can be easily removed if you so desire.

The solutions in this manual reflect the layout of the exercises to simplify checking.

A motivational award is provided on the inside back cover. It has been designed to be signed by the tutor, either a parent or a teacher.

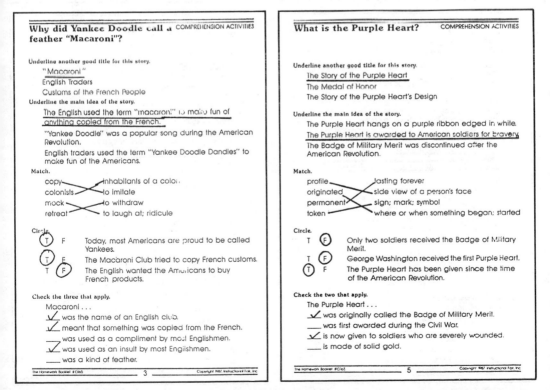

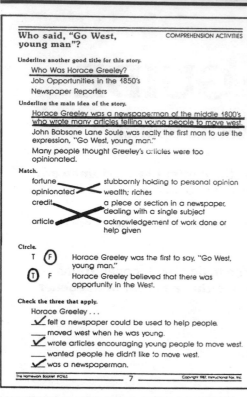

Who said, "Go West, young man"?

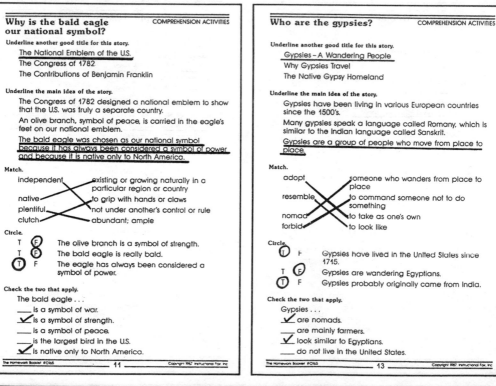

Underline another good title for this story.

Who Was Horace Greeley?

Job Opportunities in the 1850's

Newspaper Reporters

Underline the main idea of the story.

Horace Greeley was a newspaperman of the middle 1800's who wrote many articles telling young people to move west.

John Babsone Lane Soule was really the first man to use the expression, "Go West, young man."

Many people thought Greeley's articles were too opinionated.

Match.

fortune — stubbornly holding to personal opinion

opinionated — wealth; riches

credit — a piece or section in a newspaper, dealing with a single subject

article — acknowledgement of work done or help given

Circle.

T **F** Horace Greeley was the first to say, "Go West, young man."

T F Horace Greeley believed that there was opportunity in the West.

Check the three that apply.

Horace Greeley . . .

✔ felt a newspaper could be used to help people.

___ moved west when he was young.

✔ wrote articles encouraging young people to move west.

___ wanted people he didn't like to move west.

✔ was a newspaperman.

What do "SOS" and "Mayday" really mean?

COMPREHENSION ACTIVITIES

Underline another good title for this story.

International Distress Signals

Dashes and Dots

How to Get Help

Underline the main idea of the story.

Mayday is the international distress signal used in voice transmission.

The SOS distress signal was first recommended at a radio telegraph conference.

SOS and Mayday are both international signals of distress.

Match.

recommend — between two or more nations

international — passing from one person or place to another

distress — danger; difficulty

transmission — to favorably suggest

Circle.

T **F** The SOS distress signal was adopted in 1806.

T **F** SOS is the abbreviation for "save our ship."

T F Mayday is based on the French expression meaning "help me."

Check the two that apply.

SOS . . .

✔ is a convenient name for . . .---. . .---.

___ was originally based on Morse code.

✔ and Mayday are both international signals of distress.

Why is the bald eagle our national symbol?

COMPREHENSION ACTIVITIES

Underline another good title for this story.

The National Emblem of the U.S.

The Congress of 1782

The Contributions of Benjamin Franklin

Underline the main idea of the story.

The Congress of 1782 designed a national emblem to show that the U.S. was truly a separate country.

An olive branch, symbol of peace, is carried in the eagle's feet on our national emblem.

The bald eagle was chosen as our national symbol because it has always been considered a symbol of power and because it is native only to North America.

Match.

independent — existing or growing naturally in a particular region or country

native — to grip with hands or claws

plentiful — not under another's control or rule

clutch — abundant; ample

Circle.

T **F** The olive branch is a symbol of strength.

T **F** The bald eagle is really bald.

T F The eagle has always been considered a symbol of power.

Check the two that apply.

The bald eagle . . .

___ is a symbol of war.

✔ is a symbol of strength.

___ is a symbol of peace.

___ is the largest bird in the U.S.

✔ is native only to North America.

Who are the gypsies?

COMPREHENSION ACTIVITIES

Underline another good title for this story.

Gypsies – A Wandering People

Why Gypsies Travel

The Native Gypsy Homeland

Underline the main idea of the story.

Gypsies have been living in various European countries since the 1500's.

Many gypsies speak a language called Romany, which is similar to the Indian language called Sanskrit.

Gypsies are a group of people who move from place to place.

Match.

adopt — someone who wanders from place to place

resemble — to command someone not to do something

nomad — to take as one's own

forbid — to look like

Circle.

T F Gypsies have lived in the United States since 1745.

T **F** Gypsies are wandering Egyptians.

T F Gypsies probably originally came from India.

Check the two that apply.

Gypsies . . .

✔ are nomads.

___ are mainly farmers.

✔ look similar to Egyptians.

___ do not live in the United States.

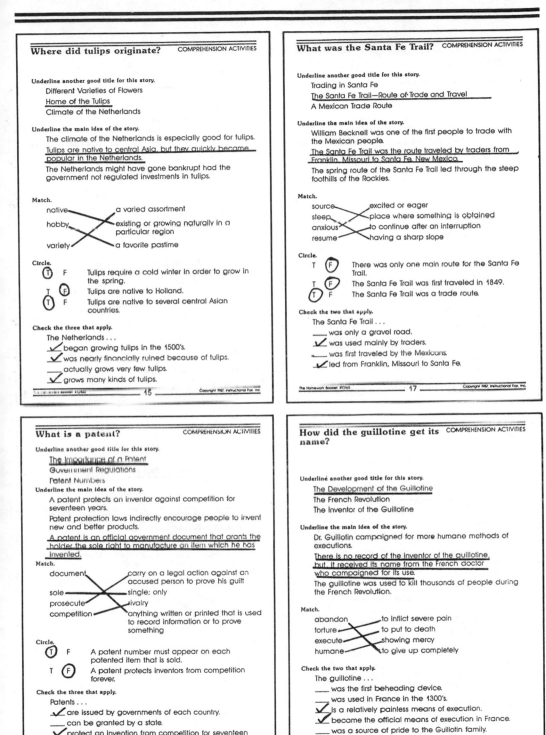

Where did tulips originate?
COMPREHENSION ACTIVITIES

Underline another good title for this story.

Different Varieties of Flowers

__Home of the Tulips__

Climate of the Netherlands

Underline the main idea of the story.

The climate of the Netherlands is especially good for tulips.

__Tulips are native to central Asia, but they quickly became__
__popular in the Netherlands.__

The Netherlands might have gone bankrupt had the government not regulated investments in tulips.

Match.

native — existing or growing naturally in a particular region

hobby — a varied assortment

variety — a favorite pastime

Circle.

(T) F   Tulips require a cold winter in order to grow in the spring.

T (F)   Tulips are native to Holland.

(T) F   Tulips are native to several central Asian countries.

Check the three that apply.

The Netherlands . . .

__✓__ began growing tulips in the 1500's.

__✓__ was nearly financially ruined because of tulips.

____ actually grows very few tulips.

__✓__ grows many kinds of tulips.

What was the Santa Fe Trail?
COMPREHENSION ACTIVITIES

Underline another good title for this story.

Trading in Santa Fe

__The Santa Fe Trail—Route of Trade and Travel__

A Mexican Trade Route

Underline the main idea of the story.

William Becknell was one of the first people to trade with the Mexican people.

__The Santa Fe Trail was the route traveled by traders from__
__Franklin, Missouri to Santa Fe, New Mexico.__

The spring route of the Santa Fe Trail led through the steep foothills of the Rockies.

Match.

source — place where something is obtained

steep — excited or eager

anxious — to continue after an interruption

resume — having a sharp slope

Circle.

T (F)   There was only one main route for the Santa Fe Trail.

T (F)   The Santa Fe Trail was first traveled in 1849.

(T) F   The Santa Fe Trail was a trade route.

Check the two that apply.

The Santa Fe Trail . . .

____ was only a gravel road.

__✓__ was used mainly by traders.

____ was first traveled by the Mexicans.

__✓__ led from Franklin, Missouri to Santa Fe.

What is a patent?
COMPREHENSION ACTIVITIES

Underline another good title for this story.

__The Importance of a Patent__

Government Regulations

Patent Numbers

Underline the main idea of the story.

A patent protects an inventor against competition for seventeen years.

Patent protection laws indirectly encourage people to invent new and better products.

__A patent is an official government document that grants the__
__holder the sole right to manufacture an item which he has__
__invented.__

Match.

document — carry on a legal action against an accused person to prove his guilt

sole — single; only

prosecute — rivalry

competition — anything written or printed that is used to record information or to prove something

Circle.

(T) F   A patent number must appear on each patented item that is sold.

T (F)   A patent protects inventors from competition forever.

Check the three that apply.

Patents . . .

__✓__ are issued by governments of each country.

____ can be granted by a state.

__✓__ protect an invention from competition for seventeen years.

____ are never extended for more than seventeen years.

__✓__ are regulated by laws.

How did the guillotine get its name?
COMPREHENSION ACTIVITIES

Underline another good title for this story.

__The Development of the Guillotine__

The French Revolution

The Inventor of the Guillotine

Underline the main idea of the story.

Dr. Guillotin campaigned for more humane methods of executions.

__There is no record of the inventor of the guillotine,__
__but it received its name from the French doctor__
__who campaigned for its use.__

The guillotine was used to kill thousands of people during the French Revolution.

Match.

abandon — to inflict severe pain

torture — to put to death

execute — showing mercy

humane — to give up completely

Check the two that apply.

The guillotine . . .

____ was the first beheading device.

____ was used in France in the 1300's.

__✓__ is a relatively painless means of execution.

__✓__ became the official means of execution in France.

____ was a source of pride to the Guillotin family.

Tutor's Guide

Copyright 1987, Instructional Fair, Inc.

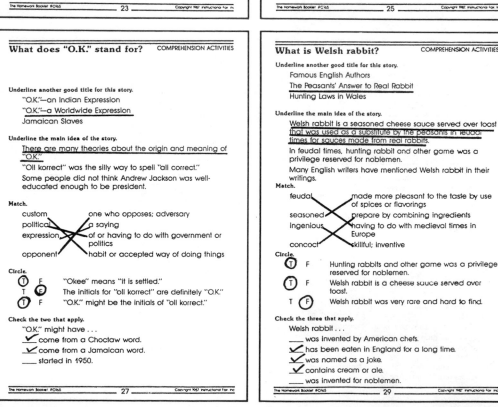

What is the origin of the word "curfew"?

Underline another good title for this story.

<u>Curfews as a Safety Device</u>
Village Fires
The Evening Bell

Underline the main idea of the story.

<u>The English word "curfew" is based on an old French term meaning "cover the fire."</u>
A thousand years ago, most homes were built of wood and had straw roofs.
Today, curfew is a time when people must get off the streets.

Match.

expression — advance notice; a word of caution
provide — to furnish; equip
seldom — not very often; rarely
warning — a saying

Circle.

T (F) A thousand years ago, people had very small fireplaces.
T (F) "Cuevre-feu" used to mean "time to go home for dinner."
(T) F The word "curfew" is based on an old French expression.

Check the two that apply.

Long ago, cuevre-feu (curfew) . . .
✔ was the time to cover the fire.
✔ was signaled by a bell.
___ was a good time to cook dinner.
___ told people they must go to bed.

Were oranges named for their color?

Underline another good title for this story.

<u>Orange—Color or Fruit?</u>
How to Cultivate Oranges
Orange Dyes

Underline the main idea of the story.

Oranges were first cultivated by the Persians.
<u>The color orange got its name from the fruit known to us as the orange.</u>
Very few things are naturally orange in color, so orange dyes had to be invented.

Match.

cultivate — raise crops by tilling, by labor, or care
misunderstanding — a failure to understand correctly
dye — material used for coloring
striking — very noticeable

Circle.

T (F) The French introduced oranges to the Persians.
T (F) Oranges are called oranges because they are orange.
(T) F The color name orange comes from the name of the orange fruit.

Check the two that apply.

Oranges . . .
___ were cultivated first in France.
✔ were cultivated first in Persia.
___ are called oranges in every language.
✔ gave the color orange its name.
___ are named after the color orange.

What does "O.K." stand for?

Underline another good title for this story.

"O.K."—an Indian Expression
<u>"O.K."—a Worldwide Expression</u>
Jamaican Slaves

Underline the main idea of the story.

<u>There are many theories about the origin and meaning of "O.K."</u>
"Oll korrect" was the silly way to spell "all correct."
Some people did not think Andrew Jackson was well-educated enough to be president.

Match.

custom — a saying
political — of or having to do with government or politics
expression — one who opposes; adversary
opponent — habit or accepted way of doing things

Circle.

(T) F "Okee" means "it is settled."
T (F) The initials for "oll korrect" are definitely "O.K."
(T) F "O.K." might be the initials of "oll korrect."

Check the two that apply.

"O.K." might have . . .
✔ come from a Choctaw word.
✔ come from a Jamaican word.
___ started in 1950.

What is Welsh rabbit?

Underline another good title for this story.

Famous English Authors
<u>The Peasants' Answer to Real Rabbit</u>
Hunting Laws in Wales

Underline the main idea of the story.

<u>Welsh rabbit is a seasoned cheese sauce served over toast that was used as a substitute by the peasants in feudal times for sauces made from real rabbits.</u>
In feudal times, hunting rabbit and other game was a privilege reserved for noblemen.
Many English writers have mentioned Welsh rabbit in their writings.

Match.

feudal — having to do with medieval times in Europe
seasoned — made more pleasant to the taste by use of spices or flavorings
ingenious — skillful; inventive
concoct — prepare by combining ingredients

Circle.

(T) F Hunting rabbits and other game was a privilege reserved for noblemen.
(T) F Welsh rabbit is a cheese sauce served over toast.
T (F) Welsh rabbit was very rare and hard to find.

Check the three that apply.

Welsh rabbit . . .
___ was invented by American chefs.
✔ has been eaten in England for a long time.
✔ was named as a joke.
✔ contains cream or ale.
___ was invented for noblemen.

Was there really a Lady Godiva?

Underline another good title for this story.

The Story of Lady Godiva's Ride

Riding to Raise Taxes

A Colorful Legend

Underline the main idea of the story.

Godgifu means "God's gift."

A Benedictine monk wrote the story of Lady Godiva in the thirteenth century.

According to legend, Lady Godiva rode through the town naked in order to lower taxes.

Match.

century ——— a saying

legend ——— charged or taxed

imposed ——— a story handed down for centuries and believed to have a historical basis

expression ——— period of 100 years

Circle.

T F Lady Godiva lived in England during the eleventh century.

T **F** The story of Lady Godiva is definitely a legend.

T **F** The story of Lady Godiva is definitely true.

Check the three that apply.

Lady Godgifu . . .

✔ was the real name of Lady Godiva.

✔ was married to Earl Leofric, Lord of Coventry.

___ was made up by a Benedictine monk.

✔ lived during the eleventh century.

What is a scarab?

Underline another good title for this story.

A Symbol of Life After Death

Nutrients in Cow Dung

Egyptian Jewels

Underline the main idea of the story.

A scarab is a type of beetle which was sacred to the ancient Egyptians because it was considered a symbol of life after death.

Symbolic scarabs made of stone or precious metals were worn as sacred charms.

The Egyptians believed the sun to be the source of all life.

Match.

sacred ——— manure

symbol ——— holy; entitled to respect and reverence

dung ——— anything nutritious or having food value

nutrient ——— that which stands for or suggests something else

Circle.

T F The Egyptians thought the pellets were symbols of the world.

T **F** A scarab is a type of cow.

T F Egyptians used scarabs as symbols of life after death.

Check the three that apply.

Scarabs . . .

✔ are beetles that lay their eggs in cow dung pellets.

✔ were believed to represent the sun.

___ were believed to represent the world.

✔ were believed to represent life after death.

___ die and are reborn.

What is the "pigeon drop"?

Underline another good title for this story.

How to Swindle a Bunko Artist

Feeding Pigeons

A Confidence Swindle

Underline the main idea of the story.

The criminal must gain the confidence of the pigeon.

The "pigeon drop" is a trick criminals use to swindle people.

The bunko artist asks a pigeon to loan him money to live on.

Match.

confidence game ——— one guilty of a crime

swindle ——— to give or take one thing in return for another

exchange ——— to cheat out of

criminal ——— a swindle that takes place by gaining the trust or confidence of someone

Circle.

T **F** A victim is called a dove.

T F The pigeon drop is a swindle.

T F The pigeon drop is a way to steal money.

Check the two that apply.

A bunko artist . . .

✔ is a confidence criminal.

___ would make a fine neighbor.

✔ robs people by tricking them.

Who invented breakfast cereals?

Underline another good title for this story.

Health Clinics

The History of Breakfast Cereals

Granola and Other Grain Products

Underline the main idea of the story.

C. W. Post started the first breakfast cereal company.

Cornflakes, All Bran, and Rice Krispies were some of William Kellogg's first breakfast cereals.

Besides other accomplishments, Dr. John Kellogg and William Kellogg invented several grain products that are now used as breakfast cereals.

Match.

toast ——— make available for selling

flatten ——— what someone usually eats or drinks

diet ——— to make or become flat

market ——— to brown the surface of something

Circle.

T F Dr. John Harvey Kellogg invented granola.

T **F** The first cereal company was started by John Kellogg.

Check the two that apply.

John H. Kellogg . . .

✔ directed a health institute.

___ believed that people should eat more meat.

✔ lived and worked in Battle Creek, Michigan.

___ founded the Toasted Corn Flake Company.

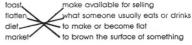

Tutor's Guide

Who invented the zipper?

Underline another good title for this story.

<u>The Development of the Zipper</u>
The Clasp Locker and Unlocker for Shoes
The B.F. Goodrich Galoshes

Underline the main idea of the story.

<u>Whitcomb L. Judson invented the first zipper and also patented many inventions for the first cars and railroads.</u>
The B.F. Goodrich Company called galoshes "zippers."
The original zipper was called a clasp locker and was rather clumsy and hard to manufacture.

Match.

clumsy — overshoes; boots
tendency — protected by an official document
galoshes — an inclination to act in a certain way
patented — awkward; not handy

Circle.

(T) F   The first zipper was very bulky compared to the zipper we now use.
T (F)   B.F. Goodrich invented the zipper.
T (F)   Zippers got their name from Whitcomb L. Judson.

Check the two that apply.

Whitcomb L. Judson . . .
___ worked for B.F. Goodrich.
___ worked for Gideon Sunback.
✓ invented the C-curity Slide Fastener.
✓ patented inventions for cars and railroads.
___ was a clothing manufacturer.

Who invented the elevator?

Underline another good title for this story.

A Dramatic Exhibition
Charging More for Hotel Rooms
<u>The First Safe Elevator</u>

Underline the main idea of the story.

Hotel owners could charge more for rooms on upper floors after the invention of the safety elevator.
<u>Elisha Graves Otis designed an elevator that would stop automatically in case the lifting rope or chain broke.</u>
In 1854, Otis demonstrated the safety elevator at a New York exhibition.

Match.

device — to lift into the air
demonstrate — to show how something works
hoist — eager
anxious — a tool or machine that has a special purpose

Circle.

(T) F   Some elevators are raised by ropes or chains.
(T) F   Hoisting devices have been used for thousands of years.
T (F)   Elisha Graves Otis invented the elevator in 1811.

Check the two that apply.

Elevators . . .
___ were invented in 1854.
___ were improved greatly by Benjamin Franklin.
✓ were made safe by Otis.
✓ were raised by pulleys.

Solve this puzzle when you have finished all of the stories.

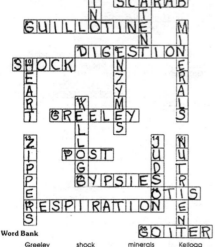

Word Bank

Greeley	shock	minerals	Kellogg
Post	zippers	nutrient	enzymes
goiter	bunko	carbohydrate	Mayday
scarab	amino	Judson	digestion
Heart	patent	guillotine	gypsies
Otis	respiration	rocks	proteins

What is digestion?

Underline another good title for this story.

<u>The Digestive Process</u>
Food Nutrients
Getting Energy to the Blood

Underline the main idea of the story.

Most of the nutrients in food are absorbed into the blood in the small intestine.
<u>Digestion is the process by which the body breaks down food into needed nutrients.</u>
Some food is digested in the stomach.

Match.

processes — to get rid of; remove
nutrient — to take in; soak up
absorb — something that promotes growth and strength
eliminate — series of steps that bring about a specific result

Circle.

T (F)   People do not need to digest their food.
(T) F   Foods are broken down to nutrients during digestion.
(T) F   Some digestion takes place in the stomach.

Check the two that apply.

Digestion . . .
✓ is the breakdown of foods.
___ occurs in the heart.
✓ occurs in the stomach.

What causes hunger?

Underline another good title for this story.

Gastric Juices

<u>The Importance of Nutrients in the Blood</u>

How to Combat Disease

Underline the main idea of the story.

<u>Hunger is caused by a lack of nutrients in the blood.</u>

The brain causes the stomach to secrete gastric juices.

During illness, the body generally does not expend energy on the digestive system.

Match.

sense — to shake or stir violently
churn — digestive liquid in the stomach
expend — to become aware of; perceive
gastric juice — to use up; spend

Circle.

T (F) During illness, a person's appetite usually increases.

(T) F A lack of nutrients in the blood causes hunger.

(T) F The brain controls feelings of hunger.

Check the two that apply.

Hunger . . .

_____ usually means the body has too little blood in the veins.

✓ is caused by a lack of nutrients in the blood.

✓ is often accompanied by stomach cramps or rumbling.

What is a vitamin?

Underline another good title for this story.

The Discovery of Vitamin C

<u>Necessary for Good Health</u>

Dairy Products

Underline the main idea of the story.

<u>Vitamins are substances our bodies need and use to stay healthy.</u>

Citrus fruits contain Vitamin C.

There are more than 20 kinds of vitamins.

Circle.

T (F) There are only eight kinds of vitamins.

(T) F The body needs vitamins in order to remain healthy.

T (F) Vitamins can only be taken in pills.

Match.

substance — mental or physical force
energy — a series of steps that bring about a specific result
process — lemon, lime, orange, grapefruit
citrus fruits — matter; material

Check the two that apply.

We . . .

_____ need large amounts of each vitamin.

✓ need many different vitamins.

✓ get vitamins by eating fruits and vegetables.

What are enzymes?

Underline another good title for this story.

Saliva

The Process of Digestion

<u>Speeding Up Chemical Changes in the Body</u>

Underline the main idea of the story.

<u>Enzymes cause chemical changes that enable the body to function properly.</u>

Saliva is produced by the salivary glands.

Saliva contains an enzyme which breaks starches down into simple sugars.

Match.

nutrient — an organ that takes elements from the blood and secretes them in a form for the body to use or throw off

gland — to change food into a form that can be used by the body

pepsin — something that promotes growth and strength; food

digest — an enzyme produced in the stomach that aids in the digestion of proteins

Circle.

(T) F Some enzymes break down nutrients so our bodies can use them.

T (F) Enzymes are sugars.

(T) F Enzymes speed up chemical changes in our bodies.

Check the three that apply.

Enzymes . . .

✓ are produced in cells.

✓ cause chemical changes.

_____ hurt our bodies.

✓ help our bodies use food.

What are proteins?

Underline another good title for this story.

How the Body Functions

<u>The Nutrient Protein</u>

Nutrients

Underline the main idea of the story.

Food gives us the substances we need to stay healthy.

<u>Proteins are a kind of nutrient that help our bodies grow and stay strong.</u>

You should include protein in your diet every day.

Circle.

(T) F Meat and cheese are high in protein.

(T) F Proteins are an important kind of nutrient.

T (F) Proteins are bad for us and we should not eat them.

Check the two that apply.

Proteins . . .

✓ are found in meat, eggs, and cheese.

✓ should be included in our diet every day.

_____ stop the body from growing.

_____ make the body feel weak.

What are amino acids?

Underline another good title for this story.

<u>Amino Acids — Building Blocks of Proteins</u>
Acids in the Body
Why the Body Needs Protein

Underline the main idea of the story.

<u>Amino acids make up proteins, which are needed by all living things.</u>
Proteins are carried by the blood to the cells.
We need twenty amino acids.

Match.

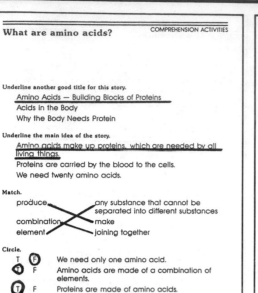

produce — joining together
combination — any substance that cannot be separated into different substances
element — make

Circle.

T **(F)** We need only one amino acid.
(T) F Amino acids are made of a combination of elements.
(T) F Proteins are made of amino acids.

Check the two that apply.

Amino acids . . .
___ are made of combinations of proteins.
✓ contain nitrogen and hydrogen.
✓ are made by living things.
___ are found mainly in water.

What are minerals?

Underline another good title for this story.

Elements
<u>Minerals We Need</u>
Vitamins

Underline the main idea of the story.

<u>Minerals are elements that our bodies need in order to stay healthy.</u>
Iodine and sulfur are minerals.
Milk is a good source of calcium.

Match.

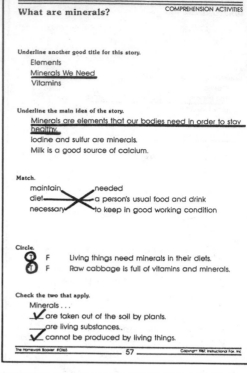

maintain — needed
diet — a person's usual food and drink
necessary — to keep in good working condition

Circle.

(T) F Living things need minerals in their diets.
(T) F Raw cabbage is full of vitamins and minerals.

Check the two that apply.

Minerals . . .
✓ are taken out of the soil by plants.
___ are living substances.
✓ cannot be produced by living things.

Why is salt iodized?

Underline another good title for this story.

Life in Coastal Regions
Salt Water
<u>Your Body Needs Iodine</u>

Underline the main idea of the story.

People who live in coastal regions usually get enough iodine from the air and water.
<u>Adding iodine to salt is a safe, easy way to make sure people get enough iodine.</u>
Iodine in large amounts is poisonous.

Match.

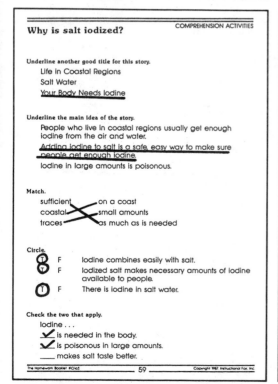

sufficient — on a coast
coastal — small amounts
traces — as much as is needed

Circle.

(T) F Iodine combines easily with salt.
(T) F Iodized salt makes necessary amounts of iodine available to people.
(T) F There is iodine in salt water.

Check the two that apply.

Iodine . . .
✓ is needed in the body.
✓ is poisonous in large amounts.
___ makes salt taste better.

What is the thyroid?

Underline another good title for this story.

Why People Gain Weight
Influence of Iodine on the Body
<u>The Thyroid and Energy</u>

Underline the main idea of the story.

A person with an underactive thyroid feels tired.
<u>The thyroid is an important gland that affects the body's energy level.</u>
A person with an overactive thyroid often loses weight.

Match.

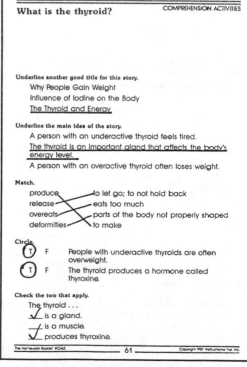

produce — to let go; to not hold back
release — eats too much
overeats — parts of the body not properly shaped
deformities — to make

Circle.

(T) F People with underactive thyroids are often overweight.
(T) F The thyroid produces a hormone called thyroxine.

Check the two that apply.

The thyroid . . .
✓ is a gland.
___ is a muscle.
✓ produces thyroxine.

What is sugar diabetes?

Underline another good title for this story.

Seeking a Cure for Diabetes

<u>Sugar Diabetes — What It Is and How It Is Treated</u>

Symptoms of Sugar Diabetes

Underline the main idea of the story.

In sugar diabetes, the body treats sugar build-up as a poison.

<u>Diabetes occurs when the body doesn't produce enough insulin or when the body doesn't react to insulin in the right way.</u>

There is no cure for sugar diabetes, but the symptoms can be controlled by treatment with insulin.

Match.

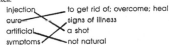

injection — a shot
cure — to get rid of; overcome; heal
artificial — not natural
symptoms — signs of illness

Circle.

(T) F   Insulin is a hormone used by the body to change sugar into energy.

T (F)   Sugar diabetes is a disease that is easily cured.

T (F)   Drinking large amounts of water will cure diabetes.

Check the two that apply.

Insulin . . .

✓ is a hormone.

___ makes a person thirsty.

✓ helps the body change sugar to energy.

___ is a cure for diabetes.

What is respiration?

Underline another good title for this story.

The Importance of Oxygen

<u>The Phases of Respiration</u>

Carbon Dioxide Wastes

Underline the main idea of the story.

Internal respiration is the exchange of fresh oxygen in the blood for carbon dioxide that has accumulated in the cells.

Fresh oxygen is inhaled by the lungs and carbon dioxide is exhaled by the lungs.

<u>Respiration is a three-phase process by which the body takes in and uses oxygen and rids itself of carbon dioxide wastes.</u>

Match.

phase — stage or period
accumulate — to collect; gather; increase
cellular — consisting of or containing cells
wastes — something left over; unused materials

Circle.

T (F)   Carbon dioxide is inhaled and oxygen is exhaled by the body.

(T) F   Oxygen is used in chemical reactions in the cells.

(T) F   There are three phases of respiration: external, internal, and cellular.

Check the two that apply.

Human cells . . .

✓ need fresh oxygen.

___ produce oxygen.

✓ produce carbon dioxide as a waste.

What is the diaphragm?

Underline another good title for this story.

<u>The Diaphragm's Role in Breathing</u>

The Human Body

Inhaling

Underline the main idea of the story.

The diaphragm separates the chest from the abdomen.

<u>The diaphragm is the main muscle used in breathing.</u>

The diaphragm is dome-shaped.

Match.

contract — to become smaller; to tighten
separate — divide
dome — an object shaped like an upside-down bowl

Circle.

(T) F   The diaphragm helps you breathe.

(T) F   The diaphragm is a large, dome-shaped muscle.

T (F)   The diaphragm is a muscle used mainly in digestion.

Check the two that apply.

The diaphragm . . .

✓ is a large muscle.

___ is a bone located in the leg.

✓ contracts and relaxes.

What is shock?

Underline another good title for this story.

Perspiring Heavily

Getting Cold

<u>A Serious Medical Problem</u>

Underline the main idea of the story.

Shock can be caused by an emotional upset.

<u>Shock is the result of the body's failure to circulate blood properly.</u>

A person could die from shock.

Match.

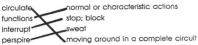

circulate — moving around in a complete circuit
functions — normal or characteristic actions
interrupt — stop; block
perspire — sweat

Circle.

(T) F   Shock is a serious medical problem.

(T) F   Shock can cause a person to die.

Check the two that apply.

Shock . . .

✓ is the result of the improper flow of blood.

✓ may cause a person's skin to feel damp and cold.

___ always results in death.

What is blood pressure?

Underline another good title for this story.

Guarding Against High Blood Pressure

Blood Pressure in the Body

How to Take Someone's Blood Pressure

Underline the main idea of the story.

Blood pressure is the pressure that the blood puts on the walls of the arteries.

Medical workers compare the patient's blood pressure with people the same age as the patient.

The arteries are lined with muscles.

Match.

typical   to be a sign of; suggest
relax   usual or average for a certain group
indicate   to make less tight or tense

Circle.

T (F)   All people have exactly the same blood pressure.

(T) F   Medical workers measure the highest and the lowest blood pressure.

(T) F   Pressure varies as the heart contracts and relaxes.

Check the two that apply.

Blood pressure . . .

___ is caused by the lungs.

✓ is caused by pressure that the blood puts on artery walls.

✓ can be an indicator of physical problems if it is too high or too low.

What are hormones?

Underline another good title for this story.

Hormones and Their Function

The Job of the Endocrine Glands

Controlling Serious Illness

Underline the main idea of the story.

Insulin regulates the sugar level in the body.

The blood carries hormones to body organs.

Hormones are powerful chemicals which are produced in one part of the body and cause an effect in another part.

Match.

hormone   part of a body not properly shaped
directly   substance formed in one organ and carried to another where it has a specific effect
deformity   in a direct manner; straight
control   to take charge of

Circle.

(T) F   Hormones control many important body functions.

T (F)   Hormones cannot be produced by glands.

(T) F   Our bodies need hormones.

Check the two that apply.

Hormones . . .

✓ are strong chemicals.

___ are produced by the intestines.

✓ are carried in the blood.

What is adrenaline?

Underline another good title for this story.

Respiratory Problems

The Hormone Adrenaline

Glands of the Body

Underline the main idea of the story.

Adrenaline is used for treating breathing problems.

Adrenaline is a hormone that is released when we experience sudden stress.

The adrenal glands release adrenaline.

Match.

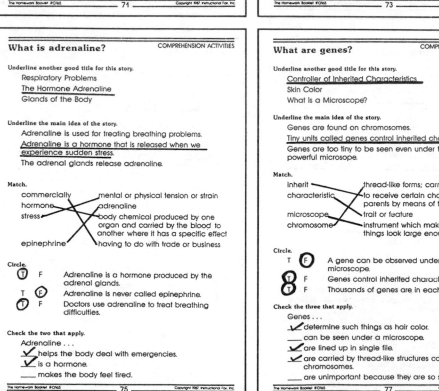

commercially   mental or physical tension or strain
hormone   adrenaline
stress   body chemical produced by one organ and carried by the blood to another where it has a specific effect
epinephrine   having to do with trade or business

Circle.

(T) F   Adrenaline is a hormone produced by the adrenal glands.

T (F)   Adrenaline is never called epinephrine.

(T) F   Doctors use adrenaline to treat breathing difficulties.

Check the two that apply.

Adrenaline . . .

✓ helps the body deal with emergencies.

✓ is a hormone.

___ makes the body feel tired.

What are genes?

Underline another good title for this story.

Controller of Inherited Characteristics

Skin Color

What Is a Microscope?

Underline the main idea of the story.

Genes are found on chromosomes.

Tiny units called genes control inherited characteristics.

Genes are too tiny to be seen even under the most powerful microscope.

Match.

inherit   thread-like forms; carriers of the genes
characteristic   to receive certain characteristics from parents by means of the genes
microscope   trait or feature
chromosome   instrument which makes very tiny things look large enough to be seen

Circle.

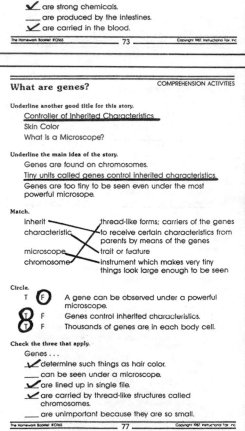

T (F)   A gene can be observed under a powerful microscope.

(T) F   Genes control inherited characteristics.

(T) F   Thousands of genes are in each body cell.

Check the three that apply.

Genes . . .

✓ determine such things as hair color.

___ can be seen under a microscope.

✓ are lined up in single file.

✓ are carried by thread-like structures called chromosomes.

___ are unimportant because they are so small.

Why do people have different skin color?

Underline another good title for this story.

The Skin
<u>Why Skin Color Varies</u>
The Sun's Effect on Skin

Underline the main idea of the story.

Skin color can vary greatly between individuals.
Melanin is a brown pigment produced in the skin.
<u>Skin color is mainly determined by the amount of melanin the body produces.</u>

Match.

melanin — to make
determiner — coloring matter in cells and tissues
pigment — that which decides or determines
produce — brown pigment

Circle.

(T) F   Skin color is determined by the amount of melanin that is produced.
(T) F   Dark skin is caused by the production of large amounts of melanin.
T (F)   Only dark-skinned people produce melanin.

Check the two that apply.

Melanin . . .
___ is skin.
___ enters the body through food.
✓ is a brown pigment.
✓ is mainly responsible for the color of the skin.

Why can't people drink salt water?

Underline another good title for this story.

The Value of Salt in the Blood
Drying Out
<u>The Effect of Salt Water on the Body</u>

Underline the main idea of the story.

If a thirsty person drinks salt water, he will continue to feel thirsty.
<u>Drinking salt water increases the salt content of the blood and causes the body to dry out.</u>
Death occurs when the body becomes too dehydrated.

Match.

occur — make greater
increase — extra
excess — take place; happen

Circle.

T (F)   You should drink salt water when you are thirsty.
(T) F   Drinking salt water increases the feeling of thirst.
(T) F   The kidneys try to "wash out" excess salt.

Check the two that apply.

Drinking salt water . . .
✓ increases the salt content of the blood.
___ tastes bad but is all right to drink.
___ decreases the feeling of thirst.
✓ can kill a person.

What is hard water?

Underline another good title for this story.

<u>Hard and Soft Water</u>
Rainwater
Filtering Water

Underline the main idea of the story.

<u>Hard water is difficult to use because it contains minerals.</u>
Hard water leaves a scale on pipes.
Soap does not dissolve easily in hard water.

Match.

mineral — natural, non-living substance
hard water — taking impurities out
filtering — to mix completely with a liquid
dissolve — water containing minerals

Circle.

(T) F   Minerals in hard water stick to pans.
T (F)   Hard water is easier to use than soft water.
(T) F   Water that contains dissolved minerals is hard water.

Check the three that apply.

Hard water . . .
___ can be used instead of soap.
✓ is harder to use than soft water.
✓ forms a hard scale on cooking pots.
✓ does not dissolve soap easily.

Wordsearch Vocabulary Review

Solve this wordsearch after you finish the whole book.

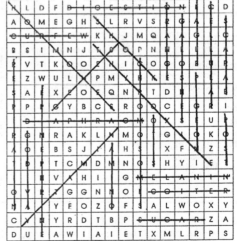

These vocabulary words are in your stories. Find and circle them in the wordsearch.

	Godiva	chromosomes	scarab
orange	melanin	epinephrine	galoshes
sugar	diaphragm	thyroxine	vitamin
curfew	hormones	respiration	amino
goiter	genes	digestion	pigeon
shock	post	Otis	eagle

The Homework Booklet Series $2.00 each

Each of these appealing, little 96-page homework booklets (6" x 9") contains a pull-out Tutor's Guide, plus an attractive award certificate to recognize successful completion of the book.

I Love Reading - Grades 1-6

This series is an excellent reinforcement for basal programs and can strongly enrich the reading, science, and social studies curricula. Each homework booklet provides a series of enjoyable short stories or articles accompanied by reading comprehension activities. Exercises are designed to sharpen skills in identifying the main idea, recalling facts and details, drawing conclusions, and using imaginative thinking. The high-interest stories make these books perfect for use with students whose reading level and grade don't match.

	Reading Level		Reading Level
IF0114	1.5	IF0144	4.1
IF0115	1.7	IF0145	4.5
IF0124	2.1	IF0154	5.1
IF0125	2.5	IF0155	5.5
IF0134	3.1	IF0164	6.1
IF0135	3.5	IF0165	6.5

Reading Comprehension - Grades 2-8

Each book contains 40 original, high-interest stories involving myths, legends, people, science, nature, and other "fun things to know." All stories are accompanied by teacher-created activities that test comprehension and stimulate thinking.

IF0113	Level 1 - Gr. 2-3
IF0123	Level 2 - Gr. 3
IF0133	Level 3 - Gr. 3-4
IF0143	Level 4 - Gr. 4-5
IF0153	Level 5 - Gr. 5-6
IF0163	Level 6 - Gr. 6-8

Readiness Skills - Ages 4 to 6

This "Little Book" Series has been designed to develop the readiness skills of pre-school to kindergarten age children. Language skills, following directions, and concept development are stressed throughout. Fun-to-do activities and colorable illustrations motivate children to make "learning" their play.

IF0101	Basic Readiness (Concept development)
IF0102	Shapes & Colors
IF0103	ABC's (Printing letters)
IF0104	Manuscript Printing
IF0105	Math (Numbers 1-10)
IF0106	Learning Games (Skill review)

The Step-By-Step Skills Series (Grades K-8)

Reading Skills - Grades K-8

IF0100	Level K-1:	Reading readiness skills
IF0122	Level 2:	Using context clues, language activities
IF0132	Level 3:	Using context clues, language activities
IF0142	Level 4:	Using context clues, determining meaning
IF0152	Level 5:	Using context clues, determining meaning
IF0162	Level 6:	Using context clues, critical thinking
IF0172	Level 7:	Using context clues, critical thinking, classifying
IF0182	Level 8:	Determining meaning, critical thinking, classifying

Language Arts & Grammar - Grades 1-8

IF0111	Level 1:	Phonics, rhyming, reading activities
IF0121	Level 2:	Phonics, rhyming, parts of speech, sentences
IF0131	Level 3:	Phonics review, basic grammar, sentence structure
IF0141	Level 4:	Parts of speech, sentence structure, punctuation
IF0151	Level 5:	Parts of speech, sentence structure, word usage
IF0161	Level 6:	Parts of speech, word usage, spelling
IF0171	Jr. High:	Parts of speech, sentence strategies, word meaning

Math - Grades 1-8

IF0110	Level 1:	Counting to 20, simple add. & sub.
IF0120	Level 2:	Simple add. & sub. regrouping
IF0130	Level 3:	Simple add. & sub., regrouping, mult., div.
IF0140	Level 4:	Add., sub., mult., div., fractions
IF0150	Level 5:	Add., sub., mult., div., fractions, decimals
IF0160	Level 6:	Mutl. & div., decimals, fractions
IF0170	Level 7:	Basic skills, decimals, fractions
IF0180	Level 8:	Signed numbers, polynomials, equivalents, geometry

This is a complete, updated list of all homework booklet titles published by Instructional Fair as of this print date. All should be readily available from the same distribution agent, location, and/or catalog source from which you secured this homework booklet. The price listed is the U.S. currency **suggested** retail as of print date. It may vary and is subject to change without notice.

Orders from individuals should be accompanied by a check or money order with appropriate sales tax and 10% shipping and handling added.

Instructional Fair, Grand Rapids, MI 49501

Solve this puzzle when you have finished all of the stories.

Word Bank

Greeley	shock	minerals	Kellogg
Post	zippers	nutrient	enzymes
goiter	bunko	carbohydrate	Mayday
scarab	amino	Judson	digestion
Heart	patent	guillotine	gypsies
Otis	respiration	rocks	proteins

What is digestion?

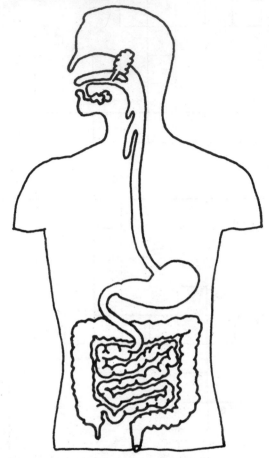

    You have heard that dairy products, like cheese and milk, are good for your bones. But how do the nutrients in these dairy products actually get to the part of the body that needs them? The body has a set of organs made especially for the digestion of food. The food is broken down into particles that go into the bloodstream and from there travel to where they are needed.

    Digestion is all of the processes by which the body breaks down the food we eat into nutrients needed by the cells. Digestion begins in the mouth, where saliva and chewing break down the food. When the food is in the stomach, some of the nutrients are absorbed into the blood. But most of the nutrients in the food are absorbed into the blood in the small intestines. Waste products are dried as they pass through the large intestine before they are eliminated.

What is digestion?

Underline another good title for this story.

The Digestive Process

Food Nutrients

Getting Energy to the Blood

Underline the main idea of the story.

Most of the nutrients in food are absorbed into the blood in the small intestine.

Digestion is the process by which the body breaks down food into needed nutrients.

Some food is digested in the stomach.

Match.

processes	to get rid of; remove
nutrient	to take in; soak up
absorb	something that promotes growth and strength
eliminate	series of steps that bring about a specific result

Circle.

T   F   People do not need to digest their food.

T   F   Foods are broken down to nutrients during digestion.

T   F   Some digestion takes place in the stomach.

Check the two that apply.

Digestion . . .

_____ is the breakdown of foods.

_____ occurs in the heart.

_____ occurs in the stomach.

45

What causes hunger?

Because hunger is often accompanied by stomach cramps and rumbling, you might think that hunger is caused by an empty stomach. But hunger is actually caused by a lack of nutrients in the blood. A special part of the brain senses when the cells have used most of the nutrients from the blood. The brain then causes the stomach to secrete gastric juices and to churn. This prepares the stomach to digest the food the body needs. The stomach is usually empty quite awhile before the nutrients in the blood are depleted enough to cause hunger.

A person who is working hard usually does not feel hungry even when the stomach is empty. The body is using all available energy in the muscles and does not expend energy on the digestive system. Also, illness often cuts the appetite because the body is using all available energy to combat the disease.

Underline another good title for this story.

Gastric Juices

The Importance of Nutrients in the Blood

How to Combat Disease

Underline the main idea of the story.

Hunger is caused by a lack of nutrients in the blood.

The brain causes the stomach to secrete gastric juices.

During illness, the body generally does not expend energy on the digestive system.

Match.

sense   to shake or stir violently

churn   digestive liquid in the stomach

expend   to become aware of; perceive

gastric juice   to use up; spend

Circle.

T   F   During illness, a person's appetite usually increases.

T   F   A lack of nutrients in the blood causes hunger.

T   F   The brain controls feelings of hunger.

Check the two that apply.

Hunger . . .

_____ usually means the body has too little blood in the veins.

_____ is caused by a lack of nutrients in the blood.

_____ is often accompanied by stomach cramps or rumbling.

What is a vitamin?

Vitamins are substances which the body needs in small amounts in order to remain healthy. There are more than 20 different kinds of vitamins. Different vitamins are necessary for growth, production of energy, and other body processes.

Meat, fruit, vegetables, and dairy products supply us with most of the vitamins we need. It was known for many hundreds of years that people who could not get certain foods became ill. But scientists isolated the first vitamin less than 100 years ago. Vitamin C was the first vitamin to be discovered. It was called "Vitamin C" because it was first discovered in citrus fruits. Some other vitamins are called A, B-complex, D, and E.

What is a vitamin?

Underline another good title for this story.

The Discovery of Vitamin C

Necessary for Good Health

Dairy Products

Underline the main idea of the story.

Vitamins are substances our bodies need and use to stay healthy.

Citrus fruits contain Vitamin C.

There are more than 20 kinds of vitamins.

Circle.

T   F   There are only eight kinds of vitamins.

T   F   The body needs vitamins in order to remain healthy.

I   F   Vitamins can only be taken in pills.

Match.

substance	mental or physical force
energy	a series of steps that bring about a specific result
process	lemon, lime, orange, grapefruit
citrus fruits	matter; material

Check the two that apply.

We . . .

_____ need large amounts of each vitamin.

_____ need many different vitamins.

_____ get vitamins by eating fruits and vegetables.

What are enzymes?

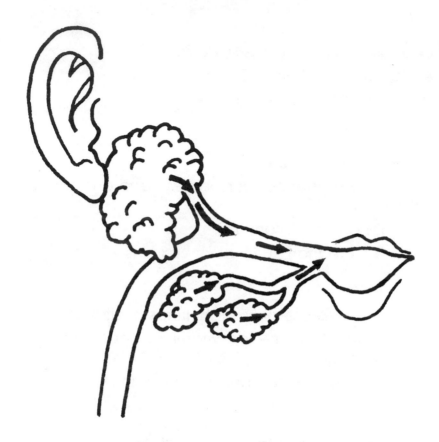

Enzymes are substances which speed up certain chemical changes in living things. Both plants and animals produce many enzymes in their cells. Saliva, for example, contains an enzyme. (Saliva is produced by salivary glands.) The enzyme in saliva breaks starches down into simple sugars. The enzyme called pepsin is produced in the stomach. It helps to digest proteins in the foods we eat. The enzyme lipase breaks down fats in the small intestine.

The body has more than 1,000 different kinds of enzymes and each has a different job to do. Enzymes are so important that without them, we would not be able to see, eat, move, or even breathe.

What are enzymes?

Underline another good title for this story.

Saliva

The Process of Digestion

Speeding Up Chemical Changes in the Body

Underline the main idea of the story.

Enzymes cause chemical changes that enable the body to function properly.

Saliva is produced by the salivary glands.

Saliva contains an enzyme which breaks starches down into simple sugars.

Match.

nutrient   an organ that takes elements from the blood and secretes them in a form for the body to use or throw off

gland   to change food into a form that can be used by the body

pepsin   something that promotes growth and strength; food

digest   an enzyme produced in the stomach that aids in the digestion of proteins

Circle.

T   F   Some enzymes break down nutrients so our bodies can use them.

T   F   Enzymes are sugars.

T   F   Enzymes speed up chemical changes in our bodies.

Check the three that apply.

Enzymes . . .

____ are produced in cells.

____ cause chemical changes.

____ hurt our bodies.

____ help our bodies use food.

What are proteins?

Food gives us the substances our bodies need to stay healthy. The "substances" found in food are called nutrients.

One very important kind of nutrient is called protein. Proteins are needed so that the body can grow and stay strong. In fact, the muscles, bones, and skin are made up mostly of proteins. So it is necessary that we include protein in our diet every day.

Some foods that are high in protein are meat, cheese, eggs, dried beans, and nuts. We should eat one or two servings of food high in protein every day.

What are proteins?

Underline another good title for this story.

How the Body Functions

The Nutrient Protein

Nutrients

Underline the main idea of the story.

Food gives us the substances we need to stay healthy.

Proteins are a kind of nutrient that help our bodies grow and stay strong.

You should include protein in your diet every day.

Circle.

T   F   Meat and cheese are high in protein.

T   F   Proteins are an important kind of nutrient.

T   F   Proteins are bad for us and we should not eat them.

Check the two that apply.

Proteins . . .

_____ are found in meat, eggs, and cheese.

_____ should be included in our diet every day.

_____ stop the body from growing.

_____ make the body feel weak.

What are amino acids?

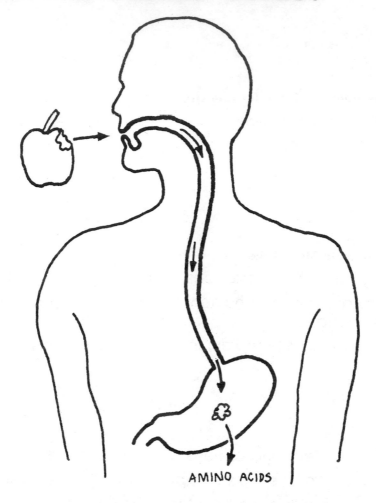

AMINO ACIDS

Amino acids are acids which make up proteins. (Proteins are needed by all living things.) Living things can make amino acids from combinations of atoms of carbon, hydrogen, oxygen, and nitrogen. Each amino acid is made of a different combination of these elements. We must have twenty amino acids to make up the proteins our bodies need. Our systems can produce many amino acids, but we must get certain amino acids from proteins in the foods we eat. Our digestive systems break down food proteins to amino acids. Then the amino acids are recombined to make the new proteins that we need. The necessary proteins are carried in the blood to the cells.

What are amino acids?

Underline another good title for this story.

Amino Acids — Building Blocks of Proteins

Acids in the Body

Why the Body Needs Protein

Underline the main idea of the story.

Amino acids make up proteins, which are needed by all living things.

Proteins are carried by the blood to the cells.

We need twenty amino acids.

Match.

produce   any substance that cannot be separated into different substances

combination   make

element   joining together

Circle.

T   F   We need only one amino acid.

T   F   Amino acids are made of a combination of elements.

T   F   Proteins are made of amino acids.

Check the two that apply.

Amino acids . . .

_____ are made of combinations of proteins.

_____ contain nitrogen and hydrogen.

_____ are made by living things.

_____ are found mainly in water.

55

What are minerals?

Minerals are elements. They cannot be produced by living things. But living things need certain minerals in order to maintain good health. Plants are able to take minerals from the soil. Animals get necessary minerals by eating plants or by eating other animals which eat plants. Most people can get all of the minerals they need by eating a balanced diet.

We need relatively large amounts of calcium, phosphorus, and iron. But minerals such as iodine and sulfur are needed only in very small amounts.

Citrus fruits, raw cabbage, salad greens, and tomatoes are not only good sources of vitamins A and C, but also provide us with calcium and iron. Whole grain biscuits and crackers are rich in both vitamins and minerals. Milk gives us vitamins and calcium.

What are minerals?

Underline another good title for this story.

Elements

Minerals We Need

Vitamins

Underline the main idea of the story.

Minerals are elements that our bodies need in order to stay healthy.

Iodine and sulfur are minerals.

Milk is a good source of calcium.

Match.

maintain	needed
diet	a person's usual food and drink
necessary	to keep in good working condition

Circle.

T　　F　　Living things need minerals in their diets.

T　　F　　Raw cabbage is full of vitamins and minerals.

Check the two that apply.

Minerals . . .

_____ are taken out of the soil by plants.

_____ are living substances.

_____ cannot be produced by living things.

Why is salt iodized?

    The human body needs traces of iodine in order to stay healthy and grow correctly. Most foods contain very little iodine. Salt water, salt air, and seafoods, however, do contain iodine. There is iodine in salt water, fresh coastal waters, and in the air in coastal regions. People who live near salt water, or who eat large amounts of seafood, usually get enough iodine from the air, water, or seafood. People in other areas could take iodine tablets or add iodine to their drinking water in order to get enough iodine. (Dosage has to be carefully measured because iodine in large amounts is poisonous.) However, an easier, safer way to distribute iodine to those who need it is to add it to table salt. Since iodine combines well with salt, it has been added to most salt sold in stores.

    The thyroid gland needs small amounts of iodine in order to produce thyroxine. Lack of iodine may cause the thyroid gland to become enlarged. A badly enlarged thyroid gland is known as "goiter."

Why is salt iodized?

Underline another good title for this story.

Life in Coastal Regions

Salt Water

Your Body Needs Iodine

Underline the main idea of the story.

People who live in coastal regions usually get enough iodine from the air and water.

Adding iodine to salt is a safe, easy way to make sure people get enough iodine.

Iodine in large amounts is poisonous.

Match.

sufficient	on a coast
ooastal	small amounts
traces	as much as is needed

Circle.

T   F   Iodine combines easily with salt.

T   F   Iodized salt makes necessary amounts of iodine available to people.

T   F   There is iodine in salt water.

Check the two that apply.

Iodine . . .

_____ is needed in the body.

_____ is poisonous in large amounts.

_____ makes salt taste better.

What is the thyroid?

The thyroid is a gland located in the neck. The thyroid takes iodine from the blood, combines it with other chemicals, and produces thyroxine. Thyroxine is a hormone which is necessary to produce energy. The thyroid stores small amounts of thyroxine and releases it into the bloodstream whenever it is needed by the cells. If the thyroid does not produce enough thyroxine, the cells cannot produce enough energy.

A person with an underactive thyroid feels tired. Such a person often overeats to try to get enough energy. Underactivity and overeating cause this person to gain large amounts of weight. A shortage of thyroxine in small children can cause physical deformities and mental retardation. A person with an overactive thyroid has too much thyroxine. Too much thyroxine causes nervousness, lack of sleep, and poor appetite. A person with an overactive thyroid often loses weight due to physical overactivity and under-eating.

What is the thyroid?

Underline another good title for this story.

Why People Gain Weight

Influence of Iodine on the Body

The Thyroid and Energy

Underline the main idea of the story.

A person with an underactive thyroid feels tired.

The thyroid is an important gland that affects the body's energy level.

A person with an overactive thyroid often loses weight.

Match.

produce	to let go; to not hold back
release	eats too much
overeats	parts of the body not properly shaped
deformities	to make

Circle.

T   F   People with underactive thyroids are often overweight.

T   F   The thyroid produces a hormone called thyroxine.

Check the two that apply.

The thyroid . . .

_____ is a gland.

_____ is a muscle.

_____ produces thyroxine.

61

What is sugar diabetes?

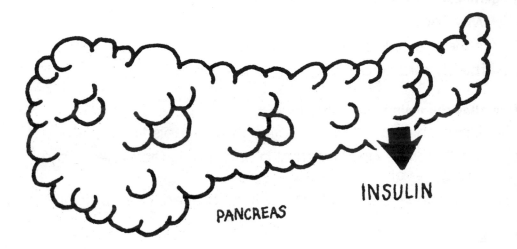

PANCREAS

INSULIN

Insulin is a hormone that is necessary for the body to change sugar into energy. Sugar diabetes is a disease that occurs when the body cannot produce enough insulin or when the body does not react to the insulin in the right way. Since the body can't use the sugar, the sugar builds up in the blood. The body then treats sugar as a poison.

Scientists have not been able to find a cure for diabetes. Doctors can only prescribe carefully measured doses of animal or artificial insulin. The insulin may be taken as pills or as injections. Treatment with insulin can control the symptoms of sugar diabetes, but cannot cure it. It is important for people with diabetes to stay on carefully planned diets.

What is sugar diabetes?

Underline another good title for this story.

Seeking a Cure for Diabetes

Sugar Diabetes — What It Is and How It Is Treated

Symptoms of Sugar Diabetes

Underline the main idea of the story.

In sugar diabetes, the body treats sugar build-up as a poison.

Diabetes occurs when the body doesn't produce enough insulin or when the body doesn't react to insulin in the right way.

There is no cure for sugar diabetes, but the symptoms can be controlled by treatment with insulin.

Match.

injection	to get rid of; overcome; heal
cure	signs of illness
artificial	a shot
symptoms	not natural

Circle.

T   F   Insulin is a hormone used by the body to change sugar into energy.

T   F   Sugar diabetes is a disease that is easily cured.

T   F   Drinking large amounts of water will cure diabetes.

Check the two that apply.

Insulin . . .

_____ is a hormone.

_____ makes a person thirsty.

_____ helps the body change sugar to energy.

_____ is a cure for diabetes.

What is respiration?

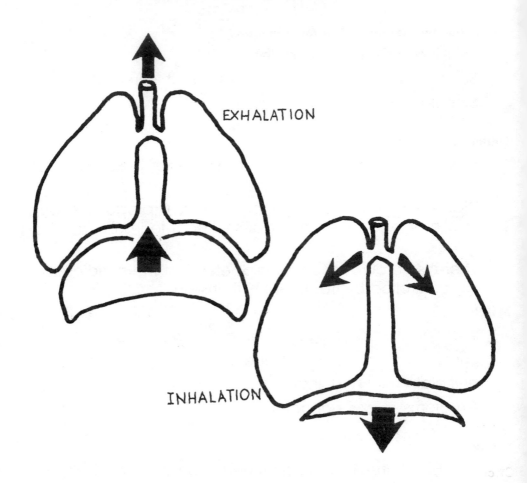

EXHALATION

INHALATION

Respiration is all of the processes by which the body takes in and uses oxygen and rids itself of carbon dioxide wastes. There are three phases of respiration.

External respiration: Fresh oxygen is inhaled, or breathed in by the lungs, and carbon dioxide is exhaled, or breathed out by the lungs.

Internal respiration: Fresh oxygen in blood is taken to the cells. Carbon dioxide wastes that have accumulated in the cells are carried away.

Cellular respiration: Oxygen is used in chemical reactions in the cells. The reactions make energy available to the cells and produce waste products of carbon dioxide and water.

What is respiration?

Underline another good title for this story.

The Importance of Oxygen

The Phases of Respiration

Carbon Dioxide Wastes

Underline the main idea of the story.

Internal respiration is the exchange of fresh oxygen in the blood for carbon dioxide that has accumulated in the cells.

Fresh oxygen is inhaled by the lungs and carbon dioxide is exhaled by the lungs.

Respiration is a three-phase process by which the body takes in and uses oxygen and rids itself of carbon dioxide wastes.

Match.

phase	something left over; unused materials
accumulate	stage or period
cellular	to collect; gather; increase
wastes	consisting of or containing cells

Circle.

T   F   Carbon dioxide is inhaled and oxygen is exhaled by the body.

T   F   Oxygen is used in chemical reactions in the cells.

T   F   There are three phases of respiration: external, internal, and cellular.

Check the two that apply.

Human cells . . .

_____ need fresh oxygen.

_____ produce oxygen.

_____ produce carbon dioxide as a waste.

What is the diaphragm?

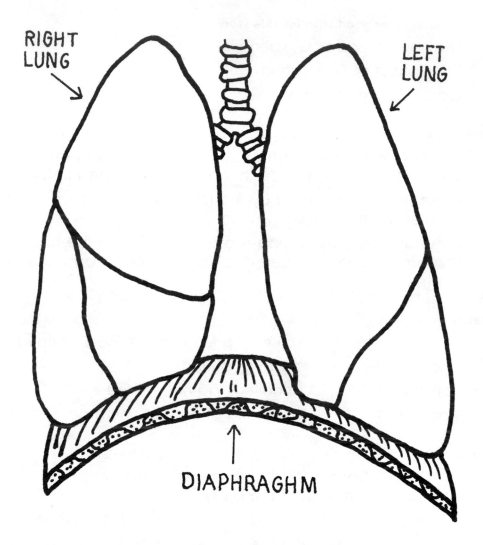

RIGHT LUNG

LEFT LUNG

DIAPHRAGHM

The diaphragm is the main muscle used in breathing. This large muscle separates the chest from the abdomen. The diaphragm helps you inhale and exhale air. It is dome-shaped and flattens downward when you take a breath. When the diaphragm contracts, the lungs pull in air. This is called inhaling. Then the diaphragm relaxes and its center moves upward, pushing carbon dioxide out of the lungs. This is called exhaling.

What is the diaphragm?

Underline another good title for this story.

The Diaphragm's Role in Breathing

The Human Body

Inhaling

Underline the main idea of the story.

The diaphragm separates the chest from the abdomen.

The diaphragm is the main muscle used in breathing.

The diaphragm is dome-shaped.

Match.

contract	an object shaped like an upside-down bowl
separate	to become smaller; to tighten
dome	divide

Circle.

T   F   The diaphragm helps you breathe.

T   F   The diaphragm is a large, dome-shaped muscle.

T   F   The diaphragm is a muscle used mainly in digestion.

Check the two that apply.

The diaphragm . . .

____ is a large muscle.

____ is a bone located in the leg.

____ contracts and relaxes.

What is shock?

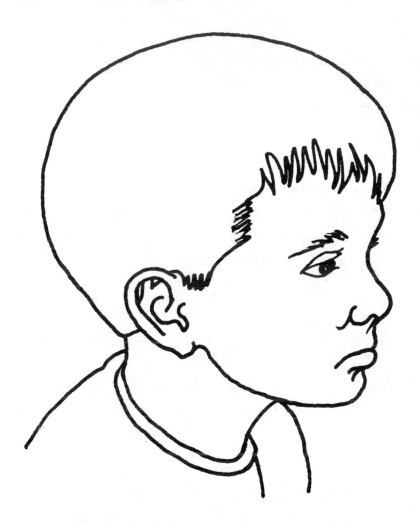

Shock is the result of the body's failure to circulate blood properly. The body may go into shock because of an extreme and sudden emotional upset. Shock can also be the result of a severe injury, such as an especially painful injury or one that involves a serious loss of blood.

When a person is in shock, he or she will perspire heavily and feel uncomfortable. Breathing becomes shallow and rapid. The person's skin is often pale, cold, and damp. A person who is in shock needs medical attention. A severe case of shock may interrupt all functions of the body, and the person could die.

What is shock?

Underline another good title for this story.

Perspiring Heavily

Getting Cold

A Serious Medical Problem

Underline the main idea of the story.

Shock can be caused by an emotional upset.

Shock is the result of the body's failure to circulate blood properly.

A person could die from shock.

Match.

circulate   normal or characteristic actions

functions   stop; block

interrupt   sweat

perspire   moving around in a complete circuit

Circle.

T   F   Shock is a serious medical problem.

T   F   Shock can cause a person to die.

Check the two that apply.

Shock . . .

_____ is the result of the improper flow of blood.

_____ may cause a person's skin to feel damp and cold.

_____ always results in death.

69

What is blood pressure?

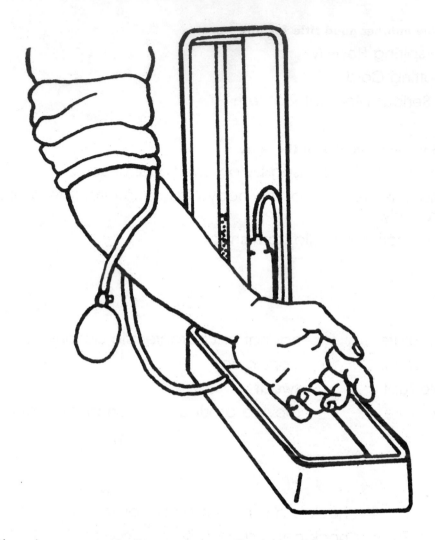

Blood pressure is the pressure that the blood puts on the walls of the arteries. The arteries are lined with muscles. The muscles first relax to allow the arteries to receive blood and then contract to force blood throughout the body. The pressure varies as the heart contracts and relaxes.

Medical workers measure both the highest and the lowest blood pressure of a patient. They compare the readings with typical blood pressure readings of people of the same age as the patient. Blood pressure readings that are either especially high or especially low usually indicate physical problems.

What is blood pressure?

Underline another good title for this story.

Guarding Against High Blood Pressure

Blood Pressure in the Body

How to Take Someone's Blood Pressure

Underline the main idea of the story.

Blood pressure is the pressure that the blood puts on the walls of the arteries.

Medical workers compare the patient's blood pressure with people the same age as the patient.

The arteries are lined with muscles.

Match.

typical	to be a sign of; suggest
relax	usual or average for a certain group
indicate	to make less tight or tense

Circle.

T   F   All people have exactly the same blood pressure.

T   F   Medical workers measure the highest and the lowest blood pressure.

T   F   Pressure varies as the heart contracts and relaxes.

Check the two that apply.

Blood pressure . . .

_____ is caused by the lungs.

_____ is caused by pressure that the blood puts on artery walls.

_____ can be an indicator of physical problems if it is too high or too low.

71

What are hormones?

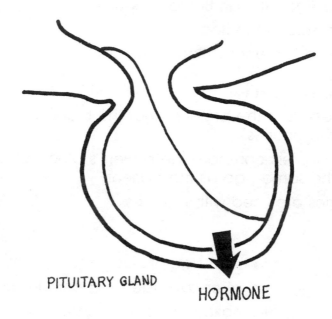

PITUITARY GLAND

HORMONE

Hormones are powerful chemicals which are produced in one part of the body and cause an effect in a different part. Hormones are very important because they control important body functions, such as the production and use of energy, body growth, and reproduction. Endocrine glands produce most of the hormones needed by our bodies. The endocrine glands deposit their hormones directly into the blood stream. The blood carries hormones to body organs. There are many hormone-producing endocrine glands. If the endocrine glands deposit too many or too few hormones into the blood stream, serious illness or physical deformities can result.

The endocrine glands produce many kinds of hormones. Insulin hormones regulate the sugar level in the body. Adrenaline hormones help the body react to emergency situations. Pituitary hormones control body growth and other important functions.

What are hormones?

Underline another good title for this story.

Hormones and Their Function

The Job of the Endocrine Glands

Controlling Serious Illness

Underline the main idea of the story.

Insulin regulates the sugar level in the body.

The blood carries hormones to body organs.

Hormones are powerful chemicals which are produced in one part of the body and cause an effect in another part.

Match.

hormone	part of a body not properly shaped
directly	substance formed in one organ and carried to another where it has a specific effect
deformity	in a direct manner; straight
control	to take charge of

Circle.

T F   Hormones control many important body functions.

T F   Hormones cannot be produced by glands.

T F   Our bodies need hormones.

Check the two that apply.

Hormones . . .

_____ are strong chemicals.

_____ are produced by the intestines.

_____ are carried in the blood.

What is adrenaline?

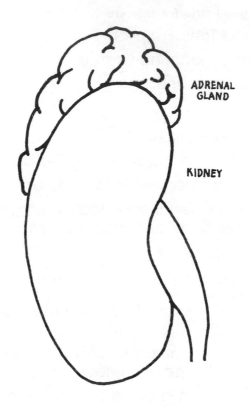

ADRENAL GLAND

KIDNEY

Have you ever heard of someone who was able to lift a car in order to save the life of someone trapped beneath it? Sometimes in a very frightening or stressful situation, we are able to do things that ordinarily we could not do. This extra rush of strength and energy comes from adrenaline.

Adrenaline is a hormone that helps our bodies react to sudden stress. When we are angry or frightened, adrenaline is released by the adrenal glands. It goes into the bloodstream. Adrenaline, sometimes called epinephrine, gives us the extra energy that we need.

Doctors use commercially produced adrenaline or epinephrine to treat patients suffering from breathing difficulties. They also use it on people who are having a severe allergic reaction and on people experiencing cardiac arrest.

What is adrenaline?

Underline another good title for this story.

Respiratory Problems

The Hormone Adrenaline

Glands of the Body

Underline the main idea of the story.

Adrenaline is used for treating breathing problems.

Adrenaline is a hormone that is released when we experience sudden stress.

The adrenal glands release adrenaline.

Match.

commercially	mental or physical tension or strain
hormone	adrenaline
stress	body chemical produced by one organ and carried by the blood to another where it has a specific effect
epinephrine	having to do with trade or business

Circle.

T   F   Adrenaline is a hormone produced by the adrenal glands.

T   F   Adrenaline is never called epinephrine.

T   F   Doctors use adrenaline to treat breathing difficulties.

Check the two that apply.

Adrenaline . . .

_____ helps the body deal with emergencies.

_____ is a hormone.

_____ makes the body feel tired.

What are genes?

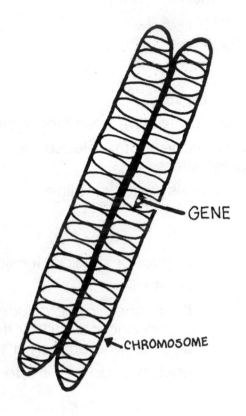

GENE

CHROMOSOME

Genes are tiny units that control the characteristics which living things inherit from their parents. Each gene is so tiny that individual genes cannot be observed even under the most powerful microscopes available.

Genes are lined up in single file on thread-like forms called chromosomes. Chromosomes carry the genes. Even though the individual genes cannot be seen, scientists have determined that thousands of different kinds of genes are arranged in the same order on a certain chromosome in each cell of the body. Each gene controls a different inherited characteristic, such as skin color, shape of the nose, or length of the eyelashes.

What are genes?

Underline another good title for this story.

Controller of Inherited Characteristics

Skin Color

What Is a Microscope?

Underline the main idea of the story.

Genes are found on chromosomes.

Tiny units called genes control inherited characteristics.

Genes are too tiny to be seen even under the most powerful microsope.

Match.

inherit   thread-like forms; carriers of the genes

characteristic   to receive certain characteristics from parents by means of the genes

microscope   trait or feature

chromosomes   instrument which makes very tiny things look large enough to be seen

Circle.

T   F   A gene can be observed under a powerful microscope.

T   F   Genes control inherited characteristics.

T   F   Thousands of genes are in each body cell.

Check the three that apply.

Genes . . .

_____ determine such things as hair color.

_____ can be seen under a microscope.

_____ are lined up in single file.

_____ are carried by thread-like structures called chromosomes.

_____ are unimportant because they are so small.

Why do people have different skin color?

Skin color varies greatly between people of different races. Skin color can also vary greatly between individuals of the same race.

The main determiner of skin color is melanin. Melanin is a brown pigment produced in the skin. Everyone's body produces melanin. But some people's bodies produce more melanin than others do. This gives them darker skin than that of people whose bodies produce little melanin pigment. Heredity determines how much melanin your body will produce.

Why do people
have different skin color?

Underline another good title for this story.

The Skin

Why Skin Color Varies

The Sun's Effect on Skin

Underline the main idea of the story.

Skin color can vary greatly between individuals.

Melanin is a brown pigment produced in the skin.

Skin color is mainly determined by the amount of melanin the body produces.

Match.

melanin	to make
determiner	coloring matter in cells and tissues
pigment	that which decides or determines
produce	brown pigment

Circle.

T   F   Skin color is determined by the amount of melanin that is produced.

T   F   Dark skin is caused by the production of large amounts of melanin.

T   F   Only dark-skinned people produce melanin.

Check the two that apply.

Melanin . . .

_____ is skin.

_____ enters the body through food.

_____ is a brown pigment.

_____ is mainly responsible for the color of the skin.

Why can't people drink salt water?

Drinking salt water increases the salt content of the blood. Although the body needs some salt, too much salt causes the body to dry out.

A person feels thirsty when there is too much salt in the blood and too little water available for the kidneys to remove the excess salt. The more salt water he drinks, the harder his body works to "wash" the salt out. He will feel even thirstier after drinking the salt water than he did before. If a person drinks too much salt water, his body will dehydrate, or dry out. Death can occur if the body becomes too dehydrated.

Why can't people drink salt water?

Underline another good title for this story.

The Value of Salt in the Blood

Drying Out

The Effect of Salt Water on the Body

Underline the main idea of the story.

If a thirsty person drinks salt water, he will continue to feel thirsty.

Drinking salt water increases the salt content of the blood and causes the body to dry out.

Death occurs when the body becomes too dehydrated.

Match.

occur	make greater
increase	extra
excess	take place; happen

Circle.

T   F   You should drink salt water when you are thirsty.

T   F   Drinking salt water increases the feeling of thirst.

T   F   The kidneys try to "wash out" excess salt.

Check the two that apply.

Drinking salt water . . .

____ increases the salt content of the blood.

____ tastes bad but is all right to drink.

____ decreases the feeling of thirst.

____ can kill a person.

What is hard water?

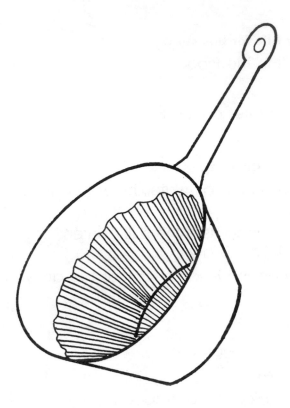

Hard water is water that contains minerals such as lime. It has that name because it is made "hard" by the minerals it contains. Water that contains little or no dissolved minerals is known as soft water. Rainwater is soft water. Hard water is harder to use than soft water. For example, it takes more soap to wash with hard water than with soft water because soap does not dissolve easily in hard water.

Hard water also leaves a bad soap scum. The minerals in hard water stick to the sides of pans when water is boiled, leaving a scale on the pans. It also leaves a scale on pipes and other equipment. Because of the disadvantages of hard water, most people try to soften hard water by filtering it in various ways.

What is hard water?

Underline another good title for this story.

Hard and Soft Water

Rainwater

Filtering Water

Underline the main idea of the story.

Hard water is difficult to use because it contains minerals.

Hard water leaves a scale on pipes.

Soap does not dissolve easily in hard water.

Match.

mineral	natural, non-living substance
hard water	taking impurities out
filtering	to mix completely with a liquid
dissolve	water containing minerals

Circle.

T　　F　　Minerals in hard water stick to pans.

T　　F　　Hard water is easier to use than soft water.

T　　F　　Water that contains dissolved minerals is hard water.

Check the three that apply.

Hard water . . .

_____ can be used instead of soap.

_____ is harder to use than soft water.

_____ forms a hard scale on cooking pots.

_____ does not dissolve soap easily.

Wordsearch Vocabulary Review

Solve this wordsearch after you finish the whole book.

H	L	D	F	D	I	G	E	S	T	I	O	N	E	C	D
A	O	M	E	G	H	S	L	R	V	S	R	G	A	E	S
C	U	R	F	E	W	K	H	J	M	Q	A	A	G	L	C
B	S	I	M	N	J	T	S	O	P	N	N	L	L	L	A
R	V	T	K	O	O	E	H	I	C	O	G	O	E	U	R
E	Z	W	U	L	N	P	M	Y	H	K	E	S	P	L	A
S	A	E	X	E	O	E	Q	N	R	T	D	H	I	A	B
P	P	P	G	Y	B	C	S	R	O	O	C	E	G	R	I
I	D	I	A	P	H	R	A	G	M	O	X	S	E	U	P
R	G	N	R	A	K	L	N	M	O	T	G	I	O	K	O
A	O	E	B	S	J	I	A	H	S	I	X	F	N	Z	S
T	D	P	T	C	M	D	M	N	O	S	H	Y	I	E	T
I	I	H	V	A	H	I	I	G	M	E	L	A	N	I	N
O	V	R	T	G	G	N	N	O	E	G	O	I	T	E	R
N	A	I	Y	F	O	Z	O	F	S	A	L	W	O	X	Y
C	V	N	Y	R	D	T	B	P	S	U	G	A	R	Z	A
D	U	E	A	W	I	A	I	E	T	X	M	L	R	P	S

These vocabulary words are in your stories. Find and circle them in the wordsearch.

	Godiva	chromosomes	scarab
orange	melanin	epinephrine	galoshes
sugar	diaphragm	thyroxine	vitamin
curfew	hormones	respiration	amino
goiter	genes	digestion	pigeon
shock	post	Otis	eagle